Boobytraps U.S. Army Instruction Manual Tactics, Techniques, and Skills

Plus

EXPLOSIVE ORDNANCE DISPOSAL Multiservice Procedures for EOD in a Joint Environment

Department of Defense

Pentagon
Publishing

CHAPTER 1

CHARACTERISTICS OF BOOBYTRAPS

Section I. INTRODUCTION

1. Purpose and Scope

   a. This manual contains procedures, techniques, and expedients for the instruction of the soldier in the assembly, use, detection, and removal of boobytraps in combat.

   b. Included are descriptions and discussions of the design and functioning characteristics of standard demolition items — firing devices, explosives, and accessories — and missiles, such as hand grenades, mortar ammunition, artillery ammunition, and bombs.

   c. This manual also contains information on a variety of items and indigenous materials useful for improvising firing devices, explosives, and pyrotechnic mixtures for guerrilla warfare applications.

   d. Factory-produced boobytraps (dirty trick devices) are described. Most of these have been developed and used in the field by foreign armies.

   e. Safety measures pertinent to boobytrapping operations are provided for the protection of troops from casualty.

   f. The contents of this manual are applicable to nuclear and non-nuclear warfare.

2. Comments

   Users of this manual are encouraged to forward comments or recommendations for changes for improvement. Comments should be referenced to the page, paragraph, and line of text. The reason for each comment should be given to insure proper interpretation and evaluation. Forward all comments directly to the Commandant, U.S. Army Engineer School, Fort Belvoir, Virginia 22060.

Section II. PRINCIPLES OF OPERATION

3. Types of Boobytraps

   A boobytrap is an explosive charge cunningly contrived to be fired by an unsuspecting person who disturbs an apparently harmless object or performs a presumably safe act. Two types are in use —improvised and manufactured. Improvised boobytraps are assembled from specially provided material or constructed from materials generally used for other purposes. Manfactured boobytraps are dirty trick devices made at a factory for issue to troops. They usually imitate some object or article that has souvenir appeal or that may be used by the target to advantage.

4. Assembling Boobytraps

A boobytrap consists of a main charge, firing device, standard base (not always used), and detonator. Another item, the universal destructor, is an adapter for installing a firing device assembly in a loaded projectile or bomb to make an improvised boobytrap. Also, firing device assemblies are often attached to the main charge by means of a length of detonating cord.

5. Boobytrap Firing Chain

THE FIRING CHAIN IS A SERIES OF INITIATIONS BEGINNING WITH A SMALL QUANTITY OF HIGHLY SENSITIVE EXPLOSIVE AND ENDING WITH A COMPARATIVELY LARGE QUANTITY OF INSENSITIVE EXPLOSIVE.

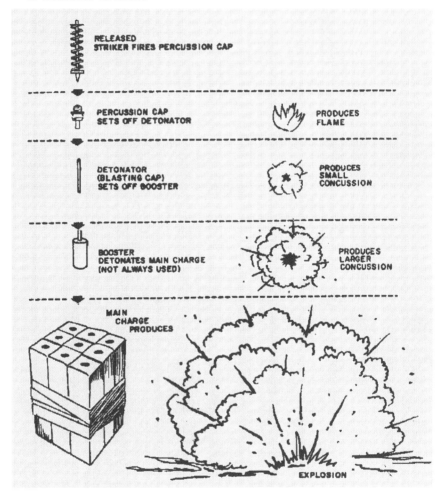

RELEASED STRIKER FIRES PERCUSSION CAP

PERCUSSION CAP SETS OFF DETONATOR — PRODUCES FLAME

DETONATOR (BLASTING CAP) SETS OFF BOOSTER — PRODUCES SMALL CONCUSSION

BOOSTER DETONATES MAIN CHARGE (NOT ALWAYS USED) — PRODUCES LARGER CONCUSSION

MAIN CHARGE PRODUCES — EXPLOSION

6. Initiating Actions

THE INITIATING ACTION STARTS THE
SERIES OF EXPLOSIONS IN THE BOOBYTRAP
FIRING CHAIN.

A. PRESSURE

WEIGHT OF FOOT
STARTS EXPLOSIVE
ACTION.

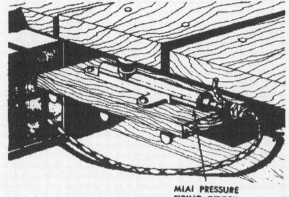

M1A1 PRESSURE
FIRING DEVICE

B. PULL

LIFTING THE
SOUVENIR STARTS
EXPLOSIVE ACTION.

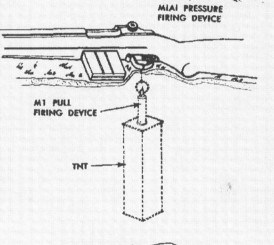

M1 PULL
FIRING DEVICE

TNT

C. PRESSURE-RELEASE

MOVING THE STONE
STARTS EXPLOSIVE
ACTION.

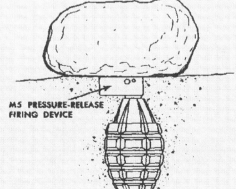

M5 PRESSURE-RELEASE
FIRING DEVICE

D. TENSION-RELEASE

RAISING LOWER SASH
STARTS EXPLOSIVE ACTION.

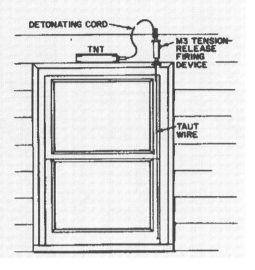

DETONATING CORD

TNT

M3 TENSION-RELEASE FIRING DEVICE

TAUT WIRE

7. Firing Device Internal Actions

A FIRING DEVICE, WHEN ACTUATED MAY
FUNCTION INTERNALLY IN MANY WAYS TO INITIATE
THE FIRING CHAIN.

A. ELECTRIC

REMOVAL OF WEDGE
BETWEEN CONTACTS
CLOSES CIRCUIT AND
FIRES ELECTRIC CAP.

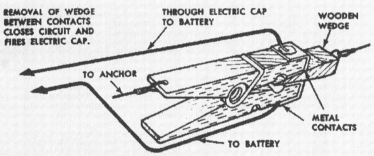

THROUGH ELECTRIC CAP
TO BATTERY

WOODEN WEDGE

TO ANCHOR

TO BATTERY

METAL CONTACTS

B. MECHANICAL

RELEASED STRIKER, DRIVEN
BY ITS SPRING, FIRES
PERCUSSION CAP.

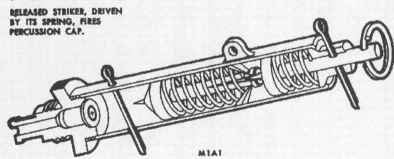

M1A1

C. PULL-FRICTION

PULLING THE CHEMICAL
PELLET THROUGH THE
CHEMICAL COMPOUND
CAUSES FLASH THAT FIRES.
THE DETONATOR.

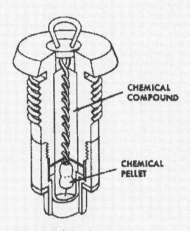

CHEMICAL
COMPOUND

CHEMICAL
PELLET

PULL-FRICTION FUZE, WEST
WW II GERMANY

D. PRESSURE-FRICTION

PRESSURE ON TOP OF THE
STRIKER FORCES ITS
CONE-SHAPED END INTO
THE PHOSPHORUS AND
GLASS MIXTURE IN THE
MATING SLEEVE, CAUSING
A FLASH THAT FIRES THE
DETONATOR

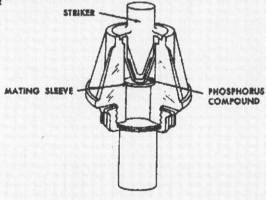

STRIKER

MATING SLEEVE

PHOSPHORUS
COMPOUND

MODEL 1952
FRANCE

E. CHEMICAL

(1) PRESSURE
PRESSURE ON THE TOP
BREAKS THE VIAL, FREEING
THE SULPHURIC ACID TO MIX
WITH THE FLASH POWDER,
PRODUCING A FLAME THAT
FIRES THE DETONATOR.

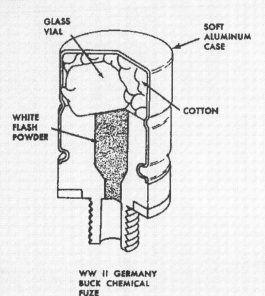

GLASS
VIAL

SOFT
ALUMINUM
CASE

WHITE
FLASH
POWDER

COTTON

WW II GERMANY
BUCK CHEMICAL
FUZE

(2) DELAY
CRUSHING THE AMPULE RELEASES
THE CHEMICAL TO CORRODE
THE RETAINING WIRE, FREEING
THE STRIKER TO FIRE THE
DETONATOR. THE DELAY IS
DETERMINED BY THE TIME
NEEDED FOR THE CHEMICAL
TO CORRODE THE RETAINING
WIRE.

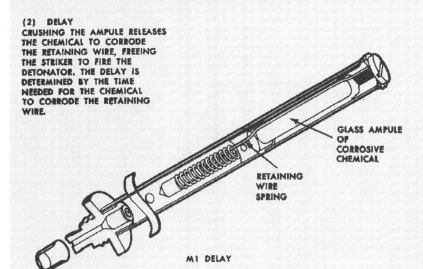

GLASS AMPULE
OF
CORROSIVE
CHEMICAL

RETAINING
WIRE
SPRING

M1 DELAY

CHAPTER 2

USE OF BOOBYTRAPS

Section I. BASIC DOCTRINE

8. Tadkal Principles

Boobytraps supplement minefields by increasing their obstacle value. They add to the confusion of the enemy, inflict' casualties, destroy material, and lower morale. Boobytraps are usually laid by specialists. All military personnel, however, are trained in handL xplosives and other boobytrapping material, so that they may, ii necessary, boobytrap a mine or install a simple boobytrap.

9. Authority

a. Army commanders issue special instructions for the use of boobytraps within their command. Supplies are authorized and provided as required to meet boobytrapping needs.

b. Army and higher commanders may delegate authority to lay boobytraps to as low as division commanders. All higher commanders, however, may revoke this authority for a definite or indefinite period, as the tactical situation may require.

e. Records of all boobytraps laid are prepared and forwarded to higher headquarters.

d. Enemy boobytraped areas, as soon as discovered, are reported to higher headquarters to keep all interested troops advised of enemy activities. If possible, all boobytraps are neutralized; otherwise they are properly marked by warning signs.

Section II. PLANNING

10. Tadkal Effects

a. The ingenious use of local resources and standard items is important in making effective boobytraps. They must be simple in construction, readily disguised, and deadly. They may produce unexpected results if conceived in sly cunning and built in various forms. Boobytraps cause uncertainty and suspicion in the mind of the enemy. They may surprise him, frustrate his plans, and inspire in his soldiers a fear of the unknown.

b. In withdrawal, boobytraps may be used in much the same way as nuisance mines. Buildings and other forms of shelter, roads, paths, diversions around obstacles, road blocks, bridges, fords, and similar areas are suitable locations for concealing boobytraps.

c. In defense, boobytraps, placed in the path of the enemy at strategic locations in sufficient numbers, may impede his progress, prevent detailed reconnoissance, and delay disarming and removal of minefields.

11. Basic Principles

Certain basic principles, as old as warfare itself, must be followed to get the optimum benefit from.boobytraps. Knowledge of these principles will aid the soldier, not only in placing boobytraps expertly, but in detecting and avoiding those of the enemy.

A. APPEARANCES
CONCEALMENT IS MANDATORY TO SUCCESS. ALL LITTER AND OTHER EVIDENCES OF BOOBYTRAPING MUST BE REMOVED.

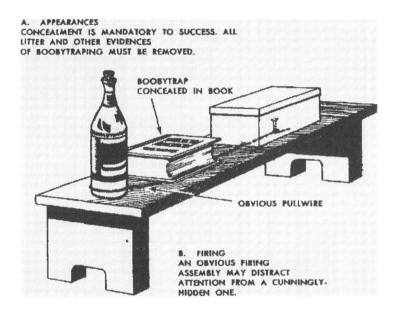

BOOBYTRAP CONCEALED IN BOOK

OBVIOUS PULLWIRE

B. FIRING
AN OBVIOUS FIRING ASSEMBLY MAY DISTRACT ATTENTION FROM A CUNNINGLY-HIDDEN ONE.

C. LIKELY AREAS
DEFILES OR OTHER CONSTRICTED AREAS ARE EXCELLENT LOCATIONS.

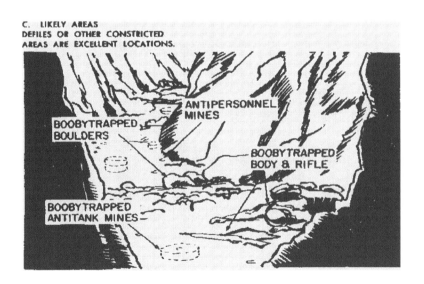

ANTIPERSONNEL MINES

BOOBYTRAPPED BOULDERS

BOOBYTRAPPED BODY & RIFLE

BOOBYTRAPPED ANTITANK MINES

D. OBSTACLES
ROAD BLOCKS, FALLEN
TREES, LITTER, ETC.,
ARE IDEAL LOCATIONS

PRESSURE-
RELEASE
FIRING
DEVICE

E. GATHERING PLACES
IN BUILDINGS, AT BUILDING ENTRANCES,
AND IN SIMILAR PLACES WHERE
SOLDIERS MAY MOVE OR
GATHER, DELAY CHARGES PAY OFF.

F. APPEAL TO CURIOSITY
BOOBYTRAPS LAID IN
BOLD POSITIONS TO DARE
THE CURIOUS GET RESULTS.

G. BLUFF
DUMMY BOOBYTRAPS, CONSISTENTLY
REPEATED, MAY ENCOURAGE CARELESSNESS.
AN OBVIOUS BOOBYTRAP MAY MASK
ANOTHER AND PERHAPS A MORE
DEADLY ONE.

EMPTY
EXPLOSIVE
CARTON

H. LURES
BOOBYTRAPS MAY BE BAITED. THE
UNEXPECTED DETONATION OF A DELAY
ACTION INCENDIARY OR EXPLOSIVE
BOOBYTRAP MAY SCATTER TROOPS OR
DETOUR THEM INTO A MORE HEAVILY LAID
AREA.

12. Location of Charges

a. Preparation. Small compact boobytraps are the most desire-
able for use in raids in enemy-held territory. Each member of a
team must carry his own supplies and be able to operate indepen-
dently. Boobytraps should be assembled, except for the attachment
of the firing device, before entering enemy territory. This will
reduce the work at the site to the minimum.

b. Location. Charges should be placed where they will do the
most damage. A charge detonated against a stone wall will expend
its force in magnified intensity away from the wall. The force of an
explosion on the ground will affect the surrounding air more if the
charge is placed on a hard surface. This deflects the explosive
wave upward. A charge detonating 6 to 10 feet above the ground
will damage a larger area than one laid on or below the surface.

c. Characteristics. Many inexpensive boobytraps, simple to make
and easy to lay, will delay and confuse the enemy more than a small
number of the expensive and complex kind. Complex mechanisms

cost more, require more care in laying, and offer little more advantage than tiie simple type.

13. Reconnaissance

Complete reconnaissance of an area is essential to good planning. Without this and the preparation of a program, boobytraps may not be used effectively. Boobytrap teams are best suited to survey a combat area to determine its boobytrapping possibilities.

14. Plan of Operation

a. The commander with authority to use boobytraps coordinates his plans with other tactical plans. Timing of boobytrap operations with movement plans is extremely essential. Boobytraps should not be laid in areas where friendly troops will remain for any appreciable length of time. Plans will indicate what is to be done, where and when it will be done, and the troops to be used. Generally, trained troops are assigned such tasks.

b. The plan authorizes the use of boobytraps and the types and densities required in specified areas, depending on the terrain, time, personnel, and material available. The completion of the detailed plan is delegated to the commander responsible for installation. Materials are obtained from unit supply stocks on the basis of the proposed action.

c. Complete coordination between the troop commander and the officer supervising boobytrap activities is essential. The area should be evacuated immediately following the completion of the job.

d. The commander installing boobytraps prepares a detailed plan indicating the site and the location, number, type, and setting. He assigns boobytrap teams to specific areas and the laying of specified types. The plan covers arrangements for supplies and transportation and designates the location where all preliminary work on boobytraps will be done. Time tables are established to insure completion of the work to comply with withdrawal phases of tactical plans.

e. In hasty withdrawal, when there is no time for planning, each team will be given a supply of material with instructions for making the best possible use of it in the time allowed.

f. Boobytrap planning must give proper consideration to all known characteristics of the enemy. Members of teams should study the personal habits of enemy soldiers, constantly devising new methods to surprise them. Repetitions may soon become a pattern easily detected by an alert enemy.

g. Withdrawal operations are the most desirable of all for laying boobytraps. When an enemy meets a boobytrap at the first obstacle, his progress throughout the area will be delayed even though no others have been laid. A few deadly boobytraps and many dummies, laid indiscriminately, can inspire great caution. Dummies, however, should be unserviceable or useless items. Never throw away material that may return to plague friendly forces!

Section III. INSTALLATION

15. Responsibilities

a. A commander authorized to use boobytraps is responsible for all within his zone of command. He will keep adequate records showing their type, number, and location, and prepare information on those laid and on practices followed by the enemy.

b. Management of boobytrap services may be delegated to the engineer staff officer.

c. Unit commanders must know the location of all boobytraps in their areas and keep all subordinates so advised. Subordinates are also responsible for reporting to higher headquarters all new information obtained on enemy boobytraps.

d. Officers responsible for laying boobytraps prepare plans, supervise preliminary preparations, and direct their installation. They forward to proper authority a detailed report of their progress, advise all concerned when changes are made, and report to engineer intelligence units the discovery of any new enemy devices or low-cunning practices.

e. Engineer and infantry units, with special training, have the responsibility of installing and neutralizing boobytraps. Since adequate numbers of trainees may not always be available, all troops are given familiarity instruction in boobytrapping.

16. Procedures

Like all activities involving explosives, boobytrapping is dangerous only because of mistakes men make. Prescribed methods must be followed explicitly in the interest of personal safety and overall effectiveness.

a. Before assemblying a boobytrap, all components should be inspected for serviceability. They must be complete and in working order. All safeties and triggering devices must be checked to insure proper action, and for rust or dents that might interfere with mechanical action.

b. If a boobytrapping plan is not available, one must be prepared on arrival at the site, so that the material obtained will be required items only. A central control point should be established in each boobytrap area where supplies may be unloaded and from which directions may be given. In areas where many boobytraps are concentrated, safe passage routes from the control point to each location must be marked clearly. Lines or tape may be useful where vegetation is heavy. The control man is the key man.

c. Several teams may operate from one control point. Each team (rarely more than two men) is assigned to a specific area and supplies are issued only as needed. Each detail commander must make certain that every man knows his job and is competent to do it. Teams will remain separated so that one may not suffer from the mistake of another. When a job is completed, all teams must report to control man before going elsewhere.

d. One person in each team is designated leader to direct all work. If possible, members of a team will avoid working close together when a boobytrap is assembled. One member should do all technical work and the other be a helper to carry supplies, provide assistance needed, and learn the skills needed.

e. Boobytraps laid during raids into enemy held territory should be small, simple, and easily installed. Each member of a party must carry the supplies he needs. The use of boobytraps under these conditions, when accurate records are impossible, may be a hazard to friendly troops if raids into the same area should become necessary.

/. Procedure for installing boobytraps is as follows:
(1) Select the site that will produce the optimum effect when the boobytrap is actuated.
(2) Lay the charge, then protect and conceal it.
(3) Anchor the boobytrap securely, with nails, wire, rope, or wedges, if necessary.
(4) Camouflage or conceal, if necessary.
(5) Teams arm boobytraps systematically, working toward a safe area.
(6) Leave the boobytrapped area clean. Carry away all items that might betray the work that has been done, such as loose dirt, empty boxes, tape, and broken vegetation. Obliterate footprints.

17. Reporting, Recording, and Marking

Boobytraps are reported and recorded for the information of tactical commanders and the protection of friendly troops from casualty. Boobytrap installations are reported and recorded as nuisance minefields, whether the area contains both boobytraps and mines or boobytraps alone.

a. Reports
(1) *Intent.* This is transmitted *by* the fastest means available consistent with signal security. It includes the location of the boobytrapped area selected, the number and type of mines to be laid (if antitank mines are boobytrapped), boobytraps to be laid, the estimated starting and completing time, and the tactical purpose. The report is initiated by the commander authorized to lay the field and forwarded to higher headquarters.
(2) *Initiation of Laying.* This report is transmitted by the fastest means available consistent with signal security. It contains the location and extent of the field, total number of mines and boobytraps to be laid, and estimated time of completion. The commander of the unit installing

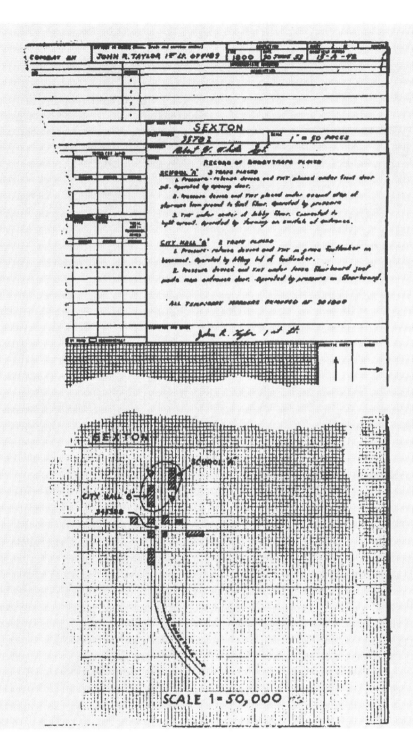

the field sends the report to the commander that directed him to lay it.

(3) *Completion.* The report of completion is transmitted by the fastest possible means. It contains the number and type of boobytraps laid, location and extent of the field or area and the time of completion. The report is forwarded to army level. When boobytraps are laid, either alone or with mines, the report of intent and the report of initiation of laying will include the estimated number of boobytraps to be placed and the report of completion, the number placed.

6. *Records.* Boobytraps are recorded as nuisance mine fields on the standard mine field record form. It is filled in as follows:

(1) The general locations are shown on the sketch, using the appropriate symbol. Boobytrapped areas or buildings are lettered serially, "A" being the nearest to the enemy.

(2) The number, types, locations, and methods of operation of boobytraps are entered in the NOTES section of the form. If space is lacking, additional sheets may be attached. If the boobytrap cannot be adequately described in a few short sentences, a sketch of minimum details will be included.

(3) The record is prepared simultaneously with the laying of the boobytrap and forwarded through channels to army level without delay. If a standard form is not available, the data required must be entered and submitted on an expedient form.

(4) Nuisance mine fields containing both mines and boobytraps are recorded as prescribed in FM 20-32. When the specific locations of boobytraps and manufactured devices cannot be accurately recorded (scattered laying in open areas) their number and type are entered in the notes section of the form and identified by grid coordinates.

e. Marking. Boobytraps are marked by special triangular signs painted red on both sides. On the side facing away from the danger area, a 3-inch diameter white disc, is centered in the triangle and the word BOOBYTRAPS is painted in white across the top in 1-inch letters. The STANAG or new sign is similar except for the 1-inch white stripe below the inscription. Signs may be made of metal, wood, plastic, or similar material. They are placed above ground, right-angled apex downwards, on wire fences, trees, or doors, windows, or other objects or by pushing the apex in the ground. These working signs are used by all troops to identify friendly boobytraps during the period preceding withdrawal from an area, or to warn friendly forces of the presence of active enemy boobytraps.

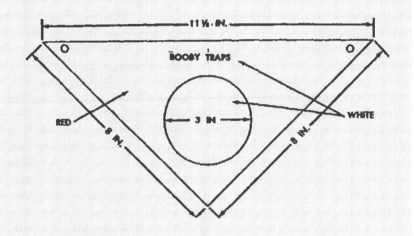

d. *Abandonment.* When abandoning a boobytrapped area to the enemy, all markers, wire, etc., are removed.

e. *Signs.* Signs are also used to mark enemy boobytraps or booby-trapped areas.

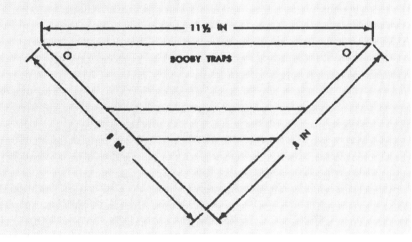

CHAPTER 3

BOOBYTRAPPING EQUIPMENT

Section I. FIRING DEVICES

18. Introduction

Many triggering devices are available for use in boobytraps. They include fuzes, igniters, and firing devices. All U.S. standard firing devices have the following advantages over improvisations; established supply, speed of installation, dependability of functioning, resistance to weather, and safety. All have a standard base coupling by which they may readily be attached to a variety of charges. For more detailed information see TM9-1375-200.

19. M1A1 Pressure Firing Device

a. Characteristics.

Case	Color	Dimensions		Internal Action	Initiating Action
		D	L		
Metal	OD	⅝ in	2¾ in	Spring-driven striker with keyhole slot release	20 lb pressure or more

Safeties	Accessories	Packaging
Safety clip and positive safety pin	3-pronged pressure head and extension rod	Five units with standard bases packed in cardboard carton. Thirty cartons shipped in wooden box.

b. Functioning.

A pressure of 20 pounds or more on the pressure cap moves the trigger pin downward until the striker spindle passes through the keyhole slot. This releases the striker to fire the percussion cap.

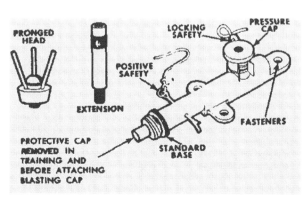

PRONGED HEAD

LOCKING SAFETY

PRESSURE CAP

POSITIVE SAFETY

EXTENSION

FASTENERS

PROTECTIVE CAP REMOVED IN TRAINING AND BEFORE ATTACHING BLASTING CAP

STANDARD BASE

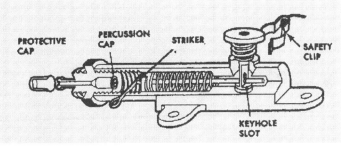

c. Installing.

(1) Remove protective cap from base and crimp on a non-electric blasting cap. *Crimper jaws should be placed* **no** *farther than # inch from open end of blasting cap.*

(2) Assemble 3-pronged pressure head and extension rod and screw in top of pressure cap, if needed.

(3) Attach firing device assembly to standard base.

(4) Attach firing device assembly to charge.

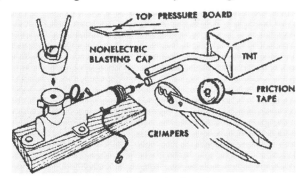

NOTE. If top pressure beard if used, allow clearance space between it and top of prongs or pressure cap.

d. Arming. Removs safety clip first and *positive pin last.*

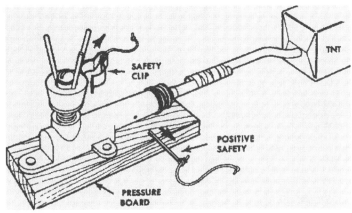

e. *Disarming.*

(1) Insert length of wire, nail, or original pin in positive safety pin hole.

(2) Replace safety clip, if available.

(3) Separate firing device and explosive block.

(3) Unscrew standard base assembly from firing device.

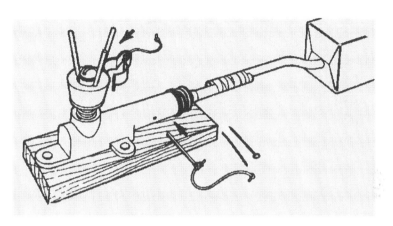

20. MI Pull Firing Device

a. *Characteristics.*

Dimensions					
Case	Color	D	L	Internal Action	Initiating Action
Metal	OD	9/16 in	3 5/16 in	Mechanical with split-head striker release	3 to 5 lb pull on trip wire

Safeties	Packaging
Locking and positive safety pins	Five units complete with standard base and two 80-ft spools of trip wire, are packed in chipboard container. Thirty chipboard containers are packed in wooden box.

b. Functioning.

A pull of 3 to 5 lb. on trip wire .withdraws tapered end of release pin from split head of striker. This frees striker to fire the percussion cap.

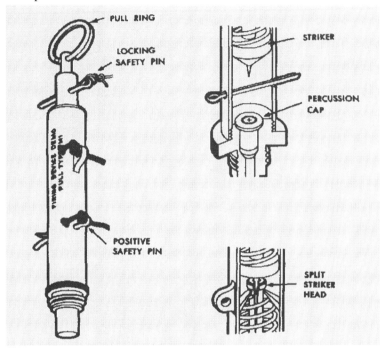

e. Installing.

(1) Remove protective cap.

(2) With crimpers, attach blasting cap to standard base. *Crimper jaws should be placed no farther than ⅜ in. from open end of blasting cap.*

(3) Attach firing device assembly to charge.

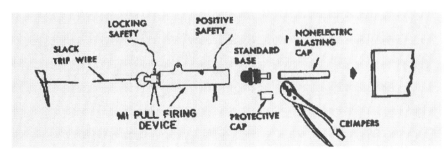

d. Arming.
    (1) Anchor trip wire and fasten other end to pull ring.
    (2) Remove locking safety pin first and *positive safety pin last.*

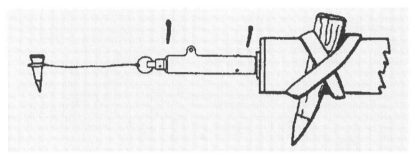

e. Disarming.
    (1) Insert nail, length of wire, or original safety pin in positive safety pin hole *first.*
    (2) Insert a similar pin in locking safety pin hole.
    (3) Cut trip wire.
    (4) Separate firing device and charge.

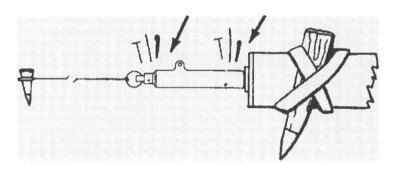

21. M3 Pull-Release Firing Device
a. Characteristics.

Case	Color	Dimensions		Internal Action	Initiating Action
		D	L		
Metal	OD	9/16 in	4 in	Mechanical with spreading striker head release	Direct pull of 6 to 10 lb or release of tension

Safeties	Packaging
Locking and positive safety pins	Five units with two 80-ft spools of trip wire in carton, and 5 cartons packed in wooden box

b. *Functioning.*
(1) Pull.
A pull of 6 to 10 lb. on taut trip wire raises release pin until shoulder passes constriction in barrel. The striker jaws then spring open, releasing striker to fire percussion cap.
(2) Tension-release.
Release of tension (cutting of taut trip wire) permits spring-driven striker to move forward, separate from release and fire percussion cap.

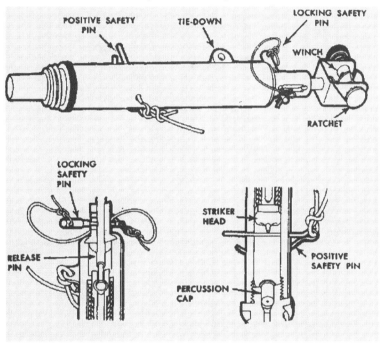

c. *Installing.*
(1) Remove protective cap.
(2) With crimpers, attach blasting cap to standard base. *Crimper jaws should be placed no farther than 1/4 in. from open end of blasting cap.*
(3) Attach firing device assembly to anchored charge (must be firm enough to withstand pull of at least 20 lb.).
(4) Secure one end of trip wire to anchor and place other end in hole in winch.
(5) With knurled knob draw up trip wire until locking safety pin is pulled into wide portion of safety pin hole.

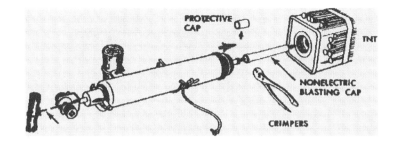

d. Arming.

    (1) With cord, remove small cotter pin from locking safety pin and withdraw locking safety pin. If it does not pull out easily, adjust winch winding.

    (2) With cord, pull out positive safety pin. This should pull out easily. If not, disassemble and inspect.

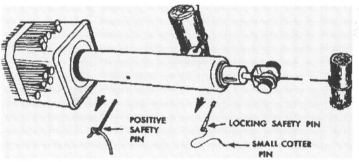

e. Disarming.

    (1) Insert length of wire, nail, or cotter pin in positive safety pin hole.

    (2) Insert length of wire, nail, of safety pin in locking safety pin hole.

    (3) Check both ends and cut trip wire.

    (4) Separate firing device from charge.

Note. Insert positive safety pin first. Cut trip wire last.

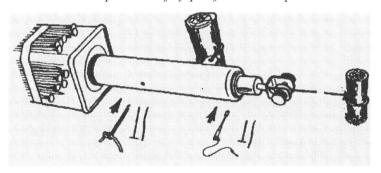

22. M5 Preiwre Releose Rring Device

a. Characteristics.

| Case | Color | Dimensions | | | Internal Action | Initiating Action |
		L	W	H,T		
Metal	OD	1 ¾	15/16	11/16	Mechanical with hinged plate release	removal of restraining wt, 5 lb or more

Accessories	Safeties	Packaging
Pressure board	Safety pin and hole for Interceptor pin	Four firing devices complete and four plywood pressure boards in paper carton. Five cartons are packaged in fiber board box and 10 of these shipped in wooden box.

b. Functioning.

Lifting or removing retaining weight releases striker to fire the percussion cap.

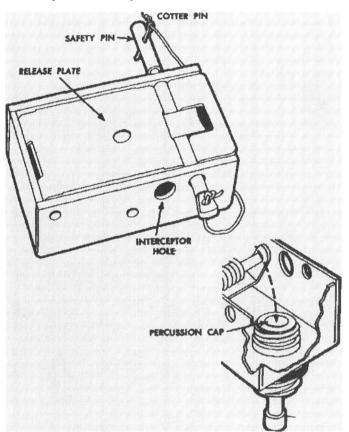

COTTER PIN

SAFETY PIN →

RELEASE PLATE

INTERCEPTOR HOLE

PERCUSSION CAP

c. *Installing.*
   (1) Insert a length of 10-gage wire in interceptor hole. Bend slightly to prevent dropping out.
   (2) Remove small cotter pin from safety pin.
   (3) Holding release plate down, replace safety pin with length of No. 18 wire. Bend wire slightly to prevent dropping out.
   (4) Remove protective cap from base and with crimpers, attach blasting cap. *Crimper jaws should be placed no farther than ¹/i inch from open end of blasting cap.*
   (5) Secure firing device assembly in charge.

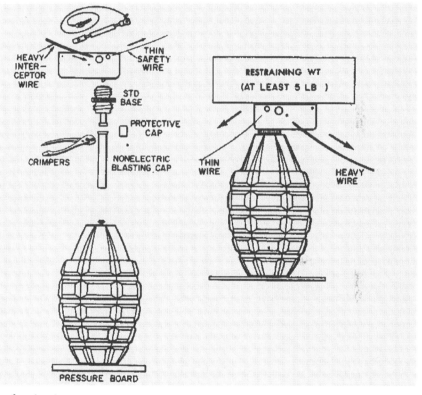

d. *Arming.*
   (1) Place restraining weight on top of firing device.
   (2) Remove thin wire from safety pin hole. If wire does not come out easily, restraining weight is either insufficient or improperly placed.
   (3) Remove heavy wire from interceptor hole. It should move freely. *Note. Withdraw thin wire first and heavy wire last. Follow arming procedure carefully*

e.   Disarming.

(1) Insert length of heavy gage wire in interceptor hole. Bend wire to prevent .dropping out. *Proceed carefully, as the slightest disturbance of the restraining weight might initiate the firing device.*

(2) Separate firing device from charge.

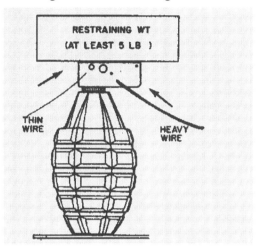

23.   15-Second Delay Detonator

a.   *Characteristics.*

This device consists of a pull-friction fuse igniter, 15-second length of fuse, and blasting cap. The blasting cap is protected by a transit cap screwed on the base.

6.   *Functioning.*

A strong pull on the pull ring draws the friction igniter through the flash compound, causing a flame which ignites the time fuse.

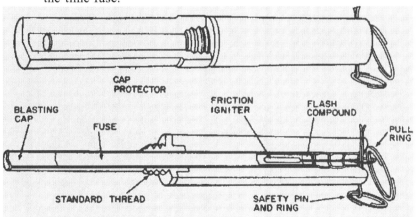

c. *Installing.*
   (1) Unscrew transit cap from base.
   (2) Secure device in charge.

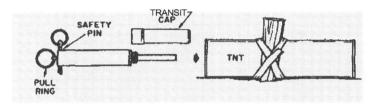

d. *Arming.*
   (1) *Manual initiation.* Remove safety pin.
   (2) *Trip wire initiation.*
   (a) Attach one end of trip wire to anchor stake and the other to pull ring.
   (b) Remove safety pin.

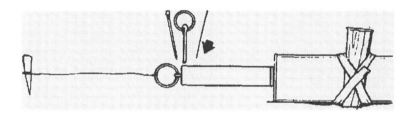

e. *Disarming.*
   (1) Insert length of wire, nail, or original safety pin in safety pin hole.
   (2) Remove trip wire.
   (3) Separate firing device from charge.

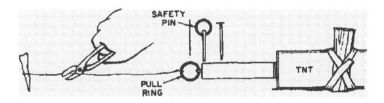

24. 8-Second Delay Detonator

   a. Characteristics.

This device consists of a pull-type fuse lighter, 8-second length of fuse, and a blasting cap. The blasting cap is protected by a transit cap, screwed on the base.

   b. Functioning.

A strong pull on the T-shaped handle draws the friction igniter through the flash compound, causing a flame that ignites the time fuse.

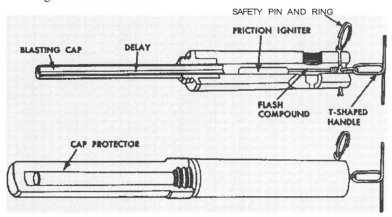

   c. Installing.

     (1) Unscrew transit cap from base.

     (2) Secure device in charge.

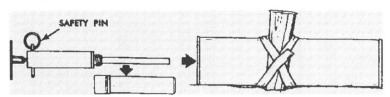

   d. Arming.

     (1) Manual initiation: Remove safety pin.

     (2) Trip wire initiation.

     (a) Attach one end of trip wire to anchor stake and the other to pull ring.

     (b) Remove safety pin.

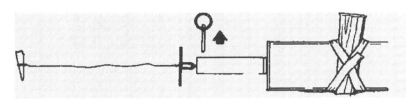

e. Disarming.
   (1) Insert length of wire, nail, or safety pin in safety pin hole.
   (2) Remove trip wire.
   (3) Separate firing device from charge.

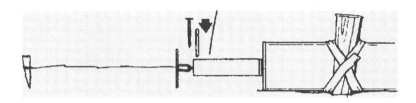

25. MI Delay Firing Device
a. Characteristics.

Case	Color	Dimensions D	Dimensions L	Internal Action	Delay
Copper and brass	Natural Metal	7/16 in	6¼ in	Mechanical with corrosive chemical release	4 min to 9 das, identified by color of safety strip

Safety	Packaging
Colored strip inserted in hole above percussion cap.	10 units—2 red, 3 white, 3 green, 1 yellow, and 1 blue—and a time delay temperature chart packed in paper board carton, 10 cartons in fiber board box, and 5 boxes in wooden box.

b. Functioning.
   Squeezing copper half of case crushes ampule, releasing chemical to corrode restraining wire and release striker.

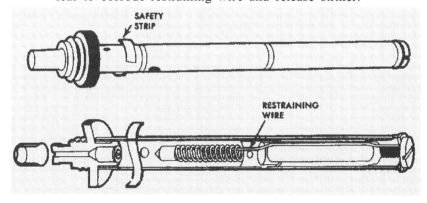

c. *Installing.*
   (1) Select device of proper delay.
   (2) Insert nail in inspection hole to make sure that firing pin has not been released.
   (3) Remove protective cap from base.
   (4) With crimpers, attach blasting cap to base. *Crimper jaws should be placed no farther than 1/4 in. from open end of blasting cap.*
   (5) Secure firing device assembly in destructor and then in charge.

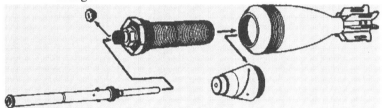

d. *Arming.*
   (1) Crush ampule by squeezing the copper portion of case.
   (2) Remove safety strip.

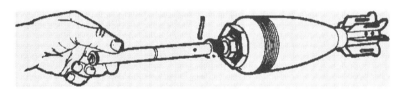

e. *Disarming.*
   There is no safe way of disarming this firing device. If disarming is necessary, insert an improvised safety pin through inspection holes.

26. **Ml Prcssuro-Raioasa Firing Devics**
   a. *Characteristics.*

| Case | Color | Dimensions | | | Internal Action | Restraining Pressure |
		L	W	Ht		
Metal	OD	3 in	2 in	2 in	Mechanical with springed latch release	3 lb or more

Safeties	Issue
Safety pin and hole for interceptor pin	Obsolete, but many are still available

6. *Functioning.*

Lifting or removing restraining weight unlatches lever, releasing striker to fire percussion cap.

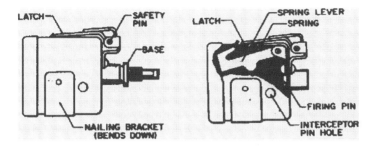

c. *Installing.*

(1) Insert a length of heavy gage wire in interceptor hole. Bend slightly to prevent dropping out.

(2) Holding down latch, remove safety pin and replace with length of thin wire.

(3) Remove protective cap from base and with crimpers attach nonelectric blasting cap. *Crimper jaws should be placed no farther than ⅜ in. from open end of blasting cap.*

(4) Assemble length of detonating cord, priming adapter, nonelectric blasting cap, and explosive block.

(5) Attach free end of detonating cord to blasting cap on M1 release device with friction tape, allowing 6 in. of detonating cord to extend beyond joint.

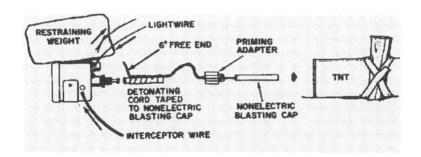

d. Arming.
  (1) Place restraining weight on top of firing device.
  (2) Remove thin wire from safety pin hole. If it does not come out easily, restraining weight is either insufficient or improperly placed.
  (3) Remove heavy wire from interceptor hole.
  Note. Proceed carefully.

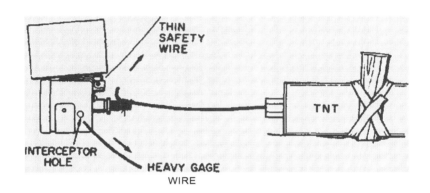

e. Disarming.
  (1) *Proceed carefully as the slightest disturbance of restraining weight might unlatch lever and detonate the mine.* Insert length of heavy gage wire in interceptor hole. Bend wire to prevent dropping out.,
  (2) Insert length of thin wire in safety pin hole, if possibile.
  (3) Separate firing device assembly and explosive charge.

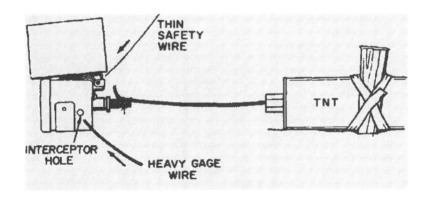

Section II. DEMOLITION MATERIALS

27. Explosives and 'Accessories (For more detailed information, see FM5-25 and TM 9-1375-200.)

  a. TNT. This is issued in **14**, 1⁄2 and 1-pound blocks in a cardboard container with lacquered metal ends. One end has a threaded cap well. Half-pound blocks are obtained by cutting a 1-pound package in the center.

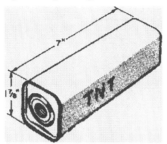

  b. Ml Chain Demolition Blocks (Tetrytol). This explosive consists of eight 21/^-pound tetrytol blocks cast 8 inches apart onto a single line of detonating cord, which extends 2 feet beyond the end blocks. All blocks have a tetryl booster in each end. Each chain is packed in a haversack, and two haversacks in a wooden box.

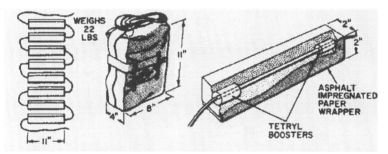

  c. M2 Demolition Block (Tetrytol). The M2 demolition block i enclosed in an asphalt impregnated paper wrapper. It has ; threaded cap well in each end. Eight blocks are packed in ; haversack, and two haversacks in a wooden box.

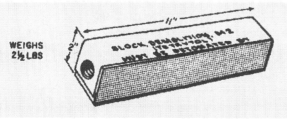

d. *MS and MS Demolition Blocks (Composition C3)*. These consist of a yellow, odorous, plastic explosive more powerful than TNT. The M3 block has a cardboard wrapper perforated around the middle for easy opening. The M5 block has a plastic container with a threaded cap well. Eight M3 or M5 blocks are packed in a haversack; and two haversacks, in a wooden box.

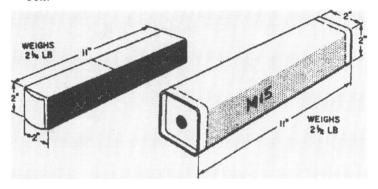

e. *M5Al Demolition Block (Composition CU)*. This is a white plastic explosive more powerful than TNT, but without the odor of C3. Each block is wrapped in plastic covering with a threaded cap well in each end. Twenty-four blocks are packed in a wooden box.

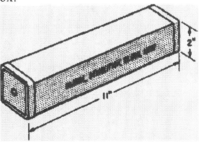

M112 Demolition Charge (Composition CU). This is composition C4 in a new package measuring 1 in. x 2 in. x 12 in. Each block has an adhesive compound on one face. Further information is not available.

g. *M118 Demolition Charge*. The M118 charge is composed of PETN and plasticizers. The detonating rate is approximately 23,000 ft. per second. Each package contains four sheets ⅛ in. x 3 in. x 12 in. Each sheet has an adhesive compound on one face. Further information is unavailable.

h. *Composition B*. Composition B is a high explosive with a relative effectiveness higher than TNT, and more sensitive.

Because of its high dentonation rate and shattering power, it is used in certain bangalore torpedoes and in shaped charges.

PETN. This is used in detonating cord. It is one of the most powerful military explosives, almost equal to nitroglycerine and RDX. In detonating cord, PETN has a velocity rate of 21,000 feet per second.

Amatol. Amatol, a mixture of ammonium nitrate and TNT, has a relative effectiveness higher than that of TNT. Amatol (80/20) is used in the bangalore torpedo.

k. *RDX.* This is the base charge in the M6 and M7 electric and nonelectric blasting caps. It is highly sensitive, and has a shattering effect second only to nitroglycerine.

. *Detonating Cord.*
   (1) *Types I and II.* These consist of a flexible braided seamless cotton tube filled with PETN. On the outside is a layer of asphalt covered by a layer of rayon with a wax gum composition finish. Type II has the larger diameter and greater tensile strength.

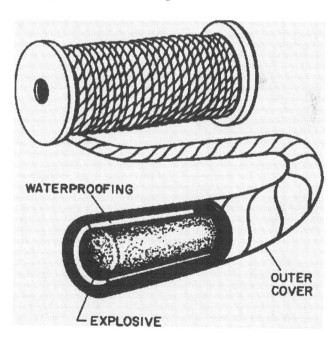

WATERPROOFING

OUTER COVER

EXPLOSIVE

(2) *Type IV.* This is similar to types I and II, except for the special smooth plastic covering designed for vigorous use and rough weather.

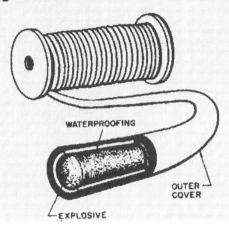

m. Blasting Time Fuse. This consists of black powder tightly wrapped in layers of fabric and waterproofing materials. It may be any color, orange being the most common. As burning rate varies from about 30 to 45 seconds per foot, each roll must be tested before using by burning and timing a 1-foot length.

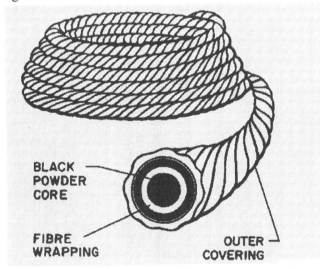

. *Safety Fuse M700. This* fuse is a dark green cord with a plastic cover, either smooth or with single pointed abrasive bands around the outside at 1-foot or 18-inch intervals and double painted abrasive bands at 5-foot or 90-inch intervals. Although the burning rate is uniform (about 40 seconds per foot), it should be tested before using by burning and timing a 1-foot length.

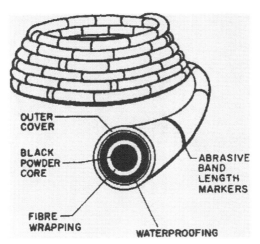

OUTER COVER

BLACK POWDER CORE

ABRASIVE BAND LENGTH MARKERS

FIBRE WRAPPING

WATERPROOFING

o. *M60 Fuse Lighter.*
  (1) *To install; Unscrew the fuse holder cap, remove shipping* plug, insert time fuse, and tighten cap.

  (2) *To reload:*

   (a) Insert primer base and primer in end of lighter housing.
   (b) Put washers and grommets in open end of fuse holder cap as shown, and screw fuse holder cap firmly on housing.
   (c) Unscrew fuse holder cap about three turns and insert a freshly cut end of time fuse into the hole in the cap until it rests against the primer.
   (d) Tighten cap.

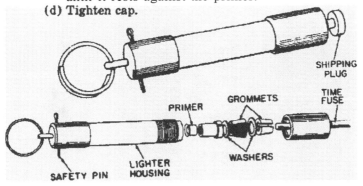

SHIPPING PLUG

TIME FUSE

GROMMETS

PRIMER

WASHERS

SAFETY PIN

LIGHTER HOUSING

(3) *To fire:*
    (a) Remove safety pin
    (b) Pull on pull ring. '
    Note. Lighter is reusable after the insertion of a new primer and the reassembly of parts.

p. Electric Blasting Caps. Electric blasting "caps have three lengths of leads—short (4 to 10 ft.), medium (12 to 14 ft), and long (50 to 100 ft). The short-circuit tab or shunt prevents accidental firing. It must be removed before the cap is connected in the firing circuit. Military blasting caps are required to insure detonation of military explosives.

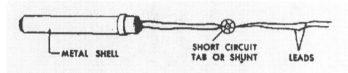

q. Nonelectric Blasting Caps. Two types are available, the No. 8 and the special M7, which resembles the No. 8 in appearance except for the expanded open end.

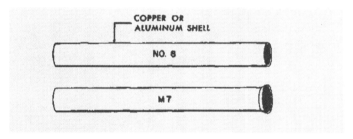

. Priming Adapter. This is a plastic device with a threaded end for securing electric and nonelectric primers in the threaded cap wells of military explosives. A groove for easy insertion **of** the electric lead wires extends the full length of the adapter.

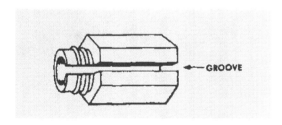

. *M10 Universal Destructor.* The destructor is used to convert loaded projectiles, missiles, and bombs into improvised charges. The destructor has booster caps containing tetryl pellets. All standard firing devices with the standard base coupler screw into the top.

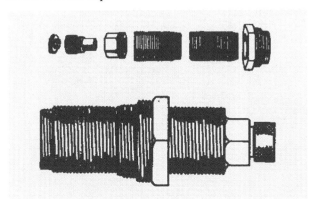

t. Antitank Mine Activator. This is a detonator designed for boobytrapping antitank mines. The top is threaded to receive all standard firing devices, and the base to screw in antitank mine activator wells.

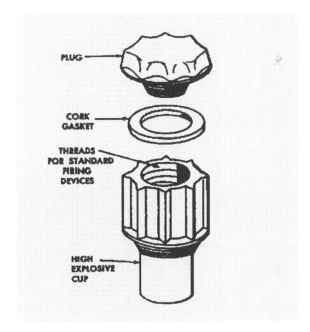

PLUG

CORK
GASKET

THREADS
FOR STANDARD
FIRING
DEVICES

HIGH
EXPLOSIVE
CUP

28. Bangalore Torpedo

The bangalore torpedo is a group of 10 loading assemblies (steel tubes filled with high explosive) with nose sleeve and connecting sleeves. The loading assemblies may be used singly, in series, or in bundles. They are primed in four ways: by a standard firing device; a standard firing device, nonelectric blasting cap, length of detonating cord, priming adapter, and nonelectric blasting cap (para 29); a standard firing device, and length of detonating cord attached by the clove hitch and two extra turns around the cap well at either end of the loading assembly; and electrical methods (para 29).

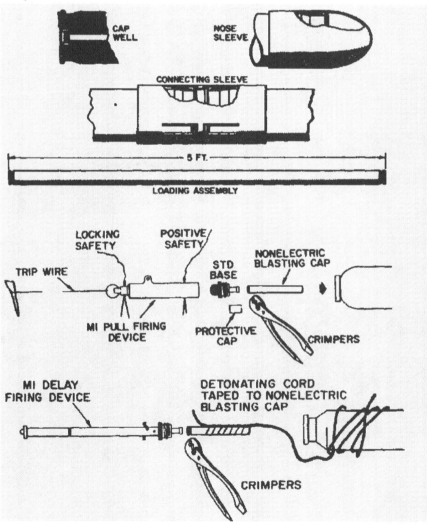

29. M2A3 Shaped Charge

This charge consists of a conical.top, conical liner, integral stand-off, threaded cap well, and ⎯⎯⎯⎯ pounds of explosive. It may be primed in three ways: by a standard firing device; a standard firing device, nonelectric blasting cap, length of detonating cord, priming adapter, and nonelectric blasting cap; and a priming adapter and electric blasting cap connected to power source.

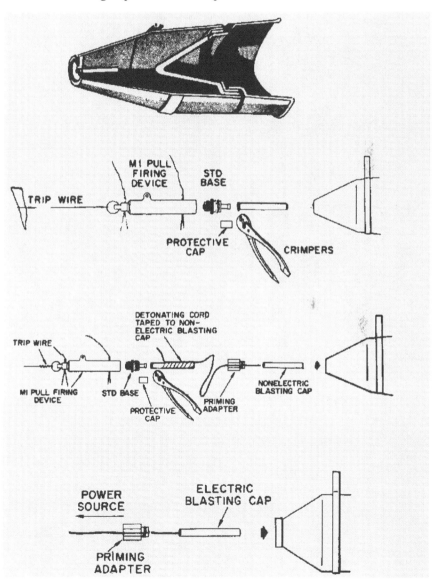

30. M3 Shaped Charge

The M3 shaped charge is a metal container with a conical top, conical liner, threaded cap well,' 30 pounds of explosive, and a metal tripod standoff. It may be primed in the same manner as the M2A3 shaped charge above.

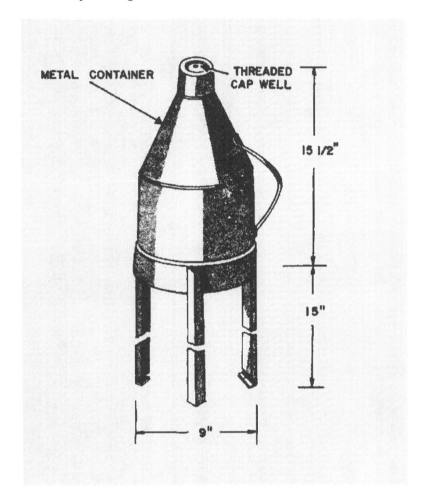

31.   Introduction

Hand grenades, bombs, and mortar and artillery ammunition have wide application as improvised explosive charges. The only portion of these useful in boobytrapping, however, are the container and its explosive filler. The fuze is replaced by a standard firing device and an M10 universal destructor—an adapter designed especially for this purpose. The number and type of missiles useful in boobytrapping, however, are not limited to the examples given below.

The M26 hand grenade, an improved model, consists of a thin metal body lined with a wire-wound fragmentation coil, fuze, and composition B explosive charge. It has a variety of applications to boobytrapping. The fuze is removed and a standard firing device is screwed directly into the fuze well or remotely connected by a length of detonating cord, priming adapter, and a nonelectric blasting cap.

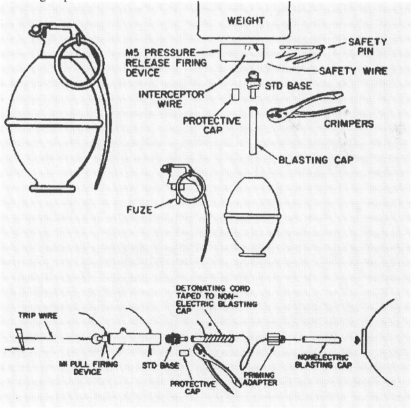

33. 81MM Mortar Sholl

This is converted by replacing the fuze with a standard firing device and a properly assembled 'destructor or by a firing device, length of detonating cord, priming adapter, nonelectric blasting cap, and a properly assembled destructor. If a destructor is not available the detonating cord and nonelectric blasting cap are packed firmly in the fuze well with C4 explosive.

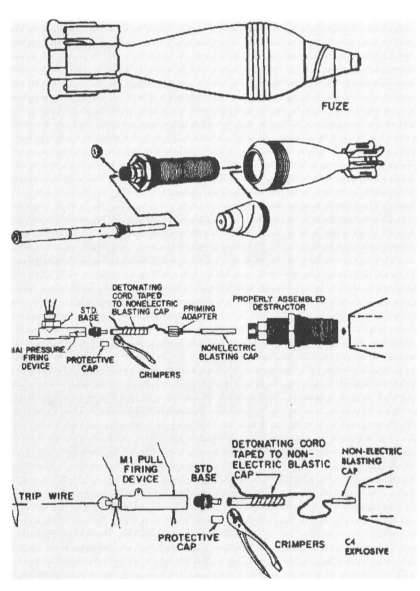

34. High Expletive Shell

The high explosive shell is readily adapted to boobytrapping. The fuze is removed and replaced by a standard firing device and a properly-assembled destructor or a standard firing device, length of detonating cord, priming adapter, nonelectric blasting cap, and a properly-assembled destructor. If a destructor is not available, the detonating cord and nonelectric blasting cap are packed firmly in the fuze well with C4 explosive.

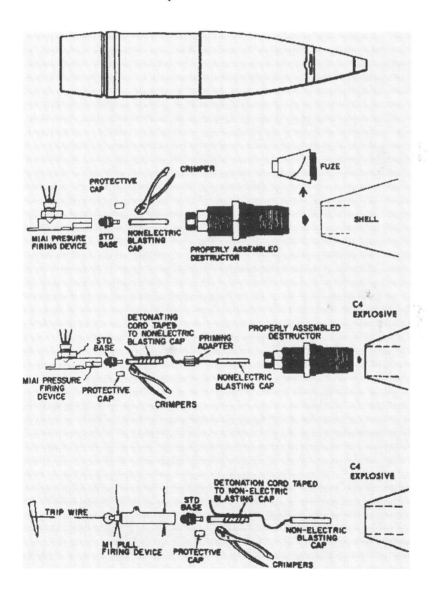

35. Bombs

These are adapted to boobytrapping in the same manner as high explosive and mortar shells. They are primed by replacing the fuze with a standard firing device and a properly-assembled destructor, or with a standard firing device, length of detonating cord, priming adapter, nonelectric blasting cap, and a properly-assembled destructor. If a destructor is not available, the detonating cord and blasting cap are packed firmly in the fuze well with C4 explosive.

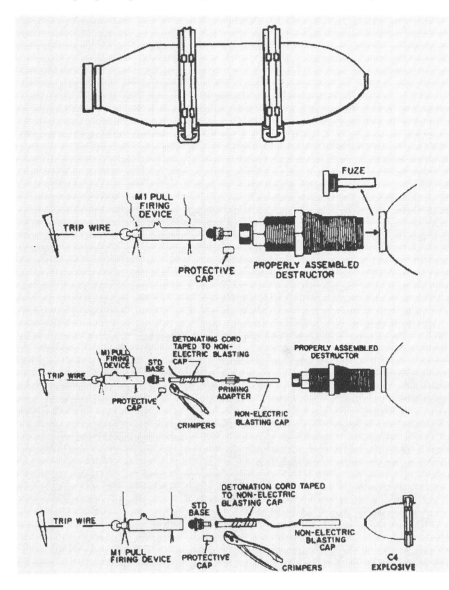

36. Antitank Mines

A land mine may be used as the main charge in a boobytrap by removing the fuze and attaching a standard pull or pressure-release firing device in an auxiliary fuze well.

(1) Remove locking safety cotter pin in M1 pull firing device and replace with length of thin wire. Bend wire slightly to prevent dropping out.

(2) Remove positive safety cotter pin and replace with length of thin wire. Bend wire slightly to prevent dropping out.

(3) Remove plastic protective cap from standard base.

(4) Assemble firing device, activator, and mine.

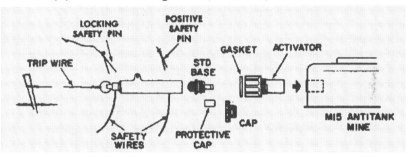

6. *Pressure-Release.*

(1) Insert length of heavy wire in interceptor hole in M5 pressure-release firing device. Bend wire slightly to prevent dropping out.

(2) Withdraw safety pin and replace with length of thin wire. Bend wire slightly to prevent dropping out.

(3) Remove plastic protective cap from standard base.

(4) Assemble firing device, activator, and mine.

Note. The firing device must be set on a firm base. A piece of masonite is issued with the M5 for this purpose.

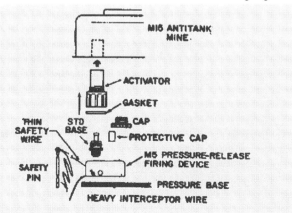

CHAPTER 4

CONSTRUCTION TECHNIQUES

Section I.   Boobytrapping Minos in Minefields

37.   Tactical Purpose

Antitank mines laid in mine fields are boobytrapped (or acti-vated) primarily to make breaching and clearing as dangerous, difficult, and time consuming as possible in order to confuse, demor-alize, and delay the enemy. Most standard U.S. antitank mines and many foreign antitank mines have auxiliary fuze wells for this purpose. See FM20-32 for more detailed information.

38.   Mothods

U.S. standard antitank mines are generally boobytrapped by means of a pull or a pressure-release firing device, or both, if desirable.

   a. Pull. Dig hole to proper depth to bury mine on firm founda-tion with top of pressure plate even with or slightly above ground level. Arm mine before boobytrapping.

(1)   *Installing.*

   (a) Remove locking safety cotter pin and replace with length of thin wire. Bend wire slightly to prevent dropping out.

   (b) Remove positive safety cotter pin and replace with length of thin wire. Bend wire slightly to prevent dropping out.

   (c) Remove protective cap from standard base and assemble firing device, activator, and mine.

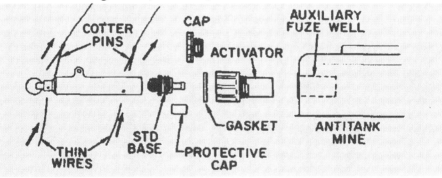

(2)   *Arming.*

   (a) Anchor one end of trip wire to stake and fasten the other to pull ring.

   (b) *Remove locking safety wire first.*

   (c) Remove positive safety but.

   (d) Camouflage.

(3) *Disarming.*

    (a) Uncover mine carefully.

    (b) Locate boobytrap assembly.

    (c) Replace positive safety *first,* then locking safety.

    (d) Cut trip wire.

    (e) Turn arming dial of mine to *safe* and remove arming plug.

    (f) Remove fuse and replace safety clip.

    (g) Replace arming plug.

    (h) Recover mine and firing device.

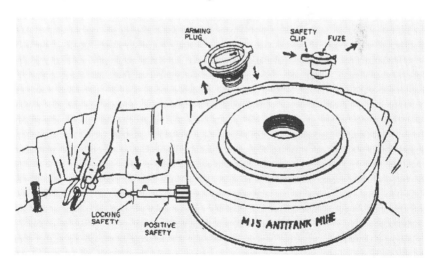

b. Pressure-Release. Dig hole to proper depth to bury mine on firm foundation, with top of pressure plate even with or slightly above ground level. .

(1) *Installing.*

(a) Insert length of heavy wire in interceptor hole. Bend wire slightly to prevent dropping out.

(b) Remove safety pin. Apply pressure on release plate until pin comes out easily.

(c) Insert length of light wire in safety pin hole and bend slightly to prevent dropping out.

(d) Remove protective cap from standard base and assemble firing device, activator, and mine.

(e) Place mine and firing assembly in hole, using pressure board to insure a solid foundation for firing device.

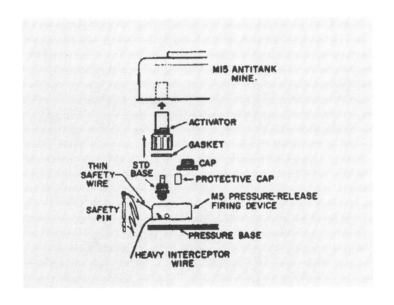

(2) *Arming.*

(a) Camouflage mine, leaving hole at side to remove safeties.

(b) Carefully remove thin safety wire *first,* then the interceptor wire.

(c) Complete camouflage.

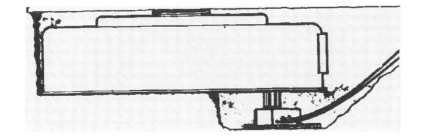

(3) *Disarming.*
(a) Uncover mine carefully.
(b) Locate boobytrap assembly.
(c) Insert length of heavy wire in interceptor hole.
(d) Turn dial on pressure plate to "S" (safe) and replace safety fork.
(e) Recover mine and firing device assembly.
(f) Remove pressure plate, unscrew detonator, and replace shipping plug.
(g) Reassemble mine.

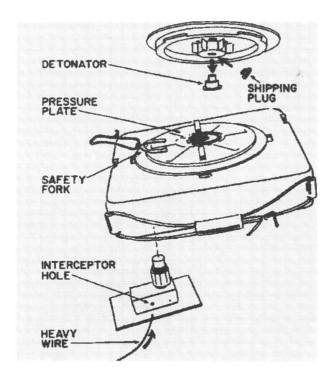

39. Boobytrapped Foreign Mines

    a. Antitank Mines.

The Communist European and Asiatic armies boobytrap mines in a much different fashion from that of the U.S. and other NATO countries. The Germans in World War II used both special antilift devices and antidisturbance fuzes, one of which has been copied by the French.

    (1) *Antilift devices,*

      (a) Russia

        1. The Russians, Communist Chinese, and North Koreans boobytrapped wooden antitank mines by laying two of them, one on top of the other, in the same hole. The mines were connected by an MUV pull fuze and a pull wire, so that the bottom mine would detonate when the top mine was lifted.

        2. The Russians in World War II also had a more sophisticated method—a special wooden antilift device, placed under the mine. This, however was readily located by probing. It consisted of an outer case, a charge, an MUV pull fuze, a pressure release lid supported on two coil springs, and a fuze access hole. Lifting the mine initiated the antilift. *This device is too dangerous to disarm.* Even though the pressure-release might be secured by a rope or length of wire, the chances of additional pull wires and boobytrap charges are too great to risk. Also deterioration of the wooden case from prolonged burial adds to the difficulty. *The best procedure is to blow all wooden antitank mines and antilifts in place.*

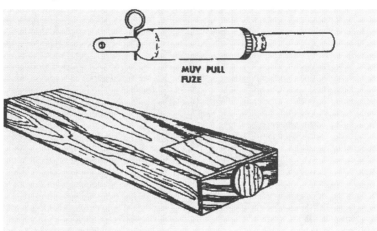

MUV PULL
FUZE

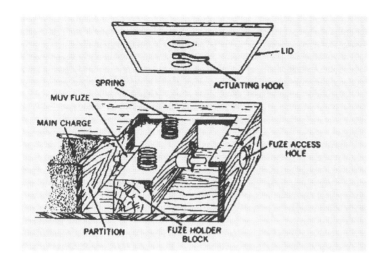

(b) Czechoslovakia. This satellite country has a wooden antitank mine (PT-Mi-D) that may prove extremely hazardous to breaching and clearing parties. Having an RO-1, pull fuze in each end, it is easily boobytrapped by means of wire anchored to a stake underneath the mine and extended through a hole in the bottom of the case to the fuze pull pin.

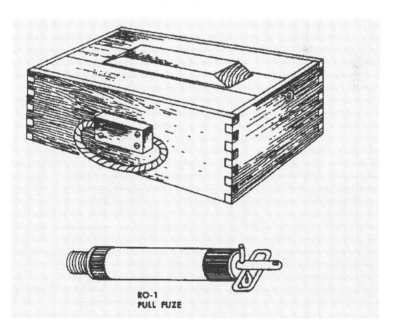

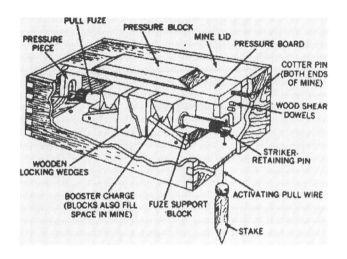

PULL FUZE
PRESSURE BLOCK
PRESSURE PIECE
MINE LID
PRESSURE BOARD
COTTER PIN (BOTH ENDS OF MINE)
WOOD SHEAR DOWELS
STRIKER-RETAINING PIN
WOODEN LOCKING WEDGES
BOOSTER CHARGE (BLOCKS ALSO FILL SPACE IN MINE)
FUZE SUPPORT BLOCK
ACTIVATING PULL WIRE
STAKE

(c) *World War II Germany.* The German armies had several pressure-release devices for boobytrapping antitank mines. In a future war in Europe, these or facsimiles may appear on any battlefield.

    1 Nipolite all explosive antilift. This consisted of two oblong blocks of moulded explosive joined together with brass bolts and recessed to contain the metal striker assembly. It may be disarmed by inserting a safety in the lower safety pin hole.

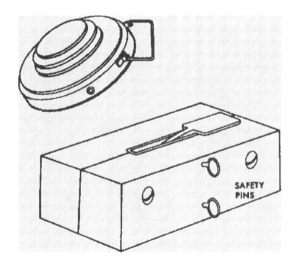

SAFETY PINS

t *EZ. SM2 (EZ U).* This device consists of an explosive charge, a pressure-release firing mechanism, a safety bar and a metal case. When the safety bar is removed, the device arms itself by means of clockwork inside the case. *This device cannot be disarmed.*

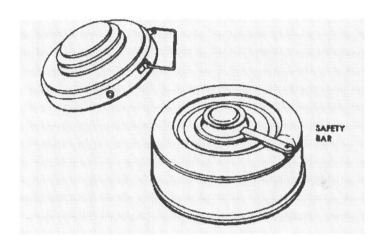

S *SFS.* This antilift consists of an explosive charge, pressure-release striker assembly, safety bar, and chemical arming equipment. A turn of the safety bar crushes the glass vial, releasing the,chemical' to dissolve the safely pellet. *This device cannot be disarmed.*

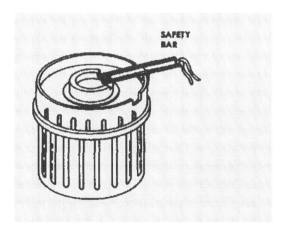

(2) **T. Mi. Z 4S and T. Mi Z 44 antidisturbance fuzes.**

(a) *Germany.* In addition to several antilift devices, the Germans developed two antidisturbance fuzes initiated by pressure or pressure-release for activating Teller mines 42 and 43. To arm, the fuze is placed in the fuze well and the pressure plate screwed down on top of the fuze, shearing the arming pin. Removal of the pressure plate initiates the pressure-release mechanism and detonates the mine. Although the T. Mi. Z 44 was an experimental model that never reached the field, copies of both fuzes are now in use in several European armies. *Mines armed with these fuzes can neither be identified by size, shape, marking, or color of the case, nor be disarmed.*

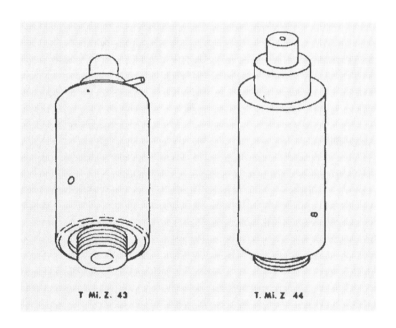

T Mi. Z. 43   T. Mi. Z 44

(b) *France.* The French have a copy of the T. Mi. Z 43 antidisturbance (pressure and pressure-release) fuze, and Teller mine 43, named models 1952 and 1948 respectively. The fuze is placed in the fuze well and the pressure plate screwed down on top, shearing the arming pin. Removing the pressure plate actuates the pressure-release element, detonating the mine.

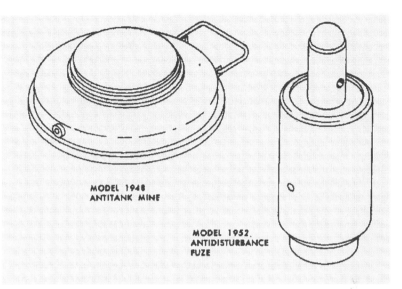

MODEL 1948
ANTITANK MINE

MODEL 1952
ANTIDISTURBANCE
FUZE

b. Antipersonnel Mines.

Antipersonnel mines are laid in antitank minefields to halt and delay enemy troops and make breaching and clearing as difficult, dangerous, and time consuming as possible. Enemy mine layers may increase this harrassment substantially by laying small blast type antipersonnel mines near the anchors and along the trip wires, which, according to procedure, must be traced from pull ring to anchor before cutting. These are extremely hazardous to breaching and clearing specialists who may detonate them unawares by the pressure of a hand, knee, or elbow on the pressure plate.

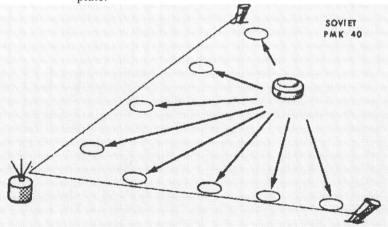

SOVIET
PMK 40

40.   AchnHflfCHJOS

Boobytraps laid in buildings and their surroundings can be very effective. Buildings are very attractive to fighting men for they provide a degree of comfort and shelter from the elements. They are also useful for headquarters where plans may be made and communications carried on with greater dispatch.

41. Immodiato Surroundings

a. Once a building has been occupied, it becomes the focal point for travel and communication from many directions. Thus the immediate vicinity becomes a potential location for boobytraps.

ft. Dwellings in sparsely populated areas often have out buildings, wood piles, fruit trees, wells, fences with gates, walks, and other locations easily rigged to wound or d< • troy careless soldiers.

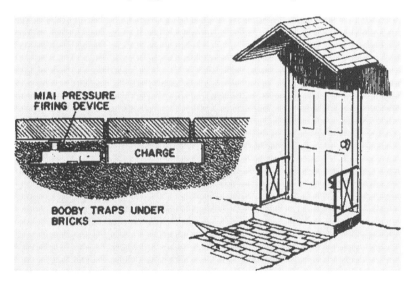

c. Delayed action charges detonated in buildings after they are occupied are extremely effective. Such charges, however, are difficult if not almost impossible to conceal, especially in large masonry and steel buildings, which may require a large quantity of explosive for serious damage or destruction. None but a most ingenious specialist, given time, help, and a wide selection of material can do this satisfactorily. In World War II, the Russians prepared such a boobytrap for the Germans. However, after long careful search, the charge and its clockwork fuze were located by means of a stethoscope. Small buildings, on the other hand, may be only moderately difficult to destroy by delayed charges.

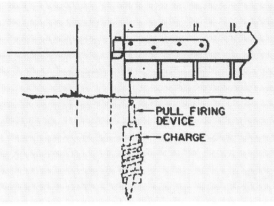

PULL FIRING DEVICE

CHARGE

42. entrances

Curiosity prompts a soldier to investigate hurriedly an interesting building in his path. Women, loot, or mere inquisitiveness **may** be the motive. His rush to be the first inside makes all entrances excellent spots for boobytraps. For the foolish, a rigging connected to the front door, side door, or back doors may be sufficient But for the experienced soldier, who may carefully seek entry to the basement first and then try to clear the building story by story, careful and ingenious effort may be required.

a. Basement Windows. Here boobytraps must be concealed to prevent detection by the enemy's breaking the pane or kicking out a door panel. Basement windows should be boobytrapped at the top or in the floor underneath.

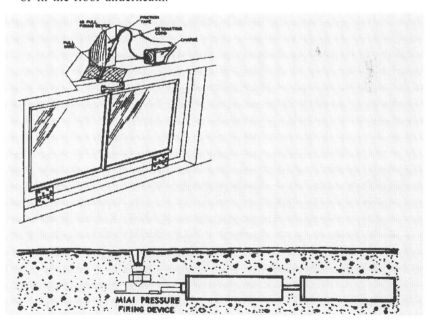

b. Upper Floor Windows. Window charges are easier concealed in the weight box behind the jamb than in the wall or under the floor. Experienced hands can remove and replace window trim without obvious damage.

(1) *Nonelectric firing.*

(a) Assemble M3 pull-release firing device, standard base, and blasting cap.

(b) Place sheet explosive in weight box.

(c) Bore hole in side jamb for pull wire.

(d) Anchor one end of pull wire to window, and thread through hole in side jamb.

(e) Attach free end of pull wire to ratchet on firing device.

(f) Arm firing device.

(g) Conceal boobytrap.

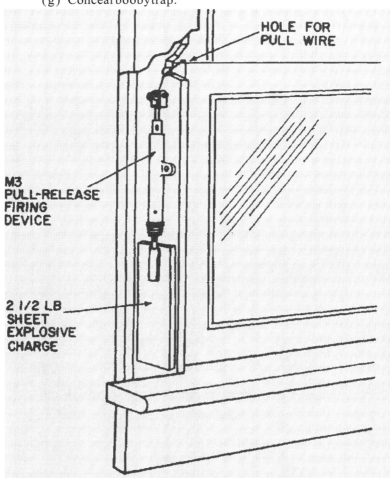

HOLE FOR PULL WIRE

M3 PULL-RELEASE FIRING DEVICE

2 1/2 LB SHEET EXPLOSIVE CHARGE

(2) *Electric firing.*

    (a) Fasten two metal brackets to side of weight box close enough to wedge two flashlight batteries between.

    (b> Place sheet explosive charge in weight box.

    (c) Insertrelectric blasting cap in charge.

    (d) Cut one leg wire and attach to lower bracket.

    (e) Cut other leg wire to proper length to twist an uninsulated loop on end and fasten to hang in .place just above top of window weight.

    (f) On a length of leg wire twist on uninsulated loop around the leg wire hanging above the weight. Thread other end through other uninsulated loop and fasten to top clamp. Tape wire to window weight.

    (g) Test circuit with galovonmeter first, then insert batteries between brackets.

    (h) Conceal boobytrap.

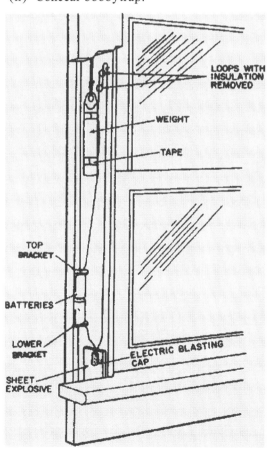

e. Doors. Improved detection methods have made the use of boobytraps on doors, with charges, firing devices, and wires exposed, a waste of time and material, except for purposes of deception. The best location is the head or side jamb, not the sill, which is often recommended. The sill is exposed, so that one experienced clearing unit may easily locate the rigging while in the jamb, it is concealed by the doorstop.

(1) *Head jamb rigging.*

   (a) Assemble M1 pull firing device, standard base, and nonelectric blasting cap.

   (b) Assemble length of detonating cord, priming adapter, nonelectric blasting cap and explosive block.

   (c) Attach firing device firmly to stud and tape free end of length of detonating cord to nonelectric blasting cap.

   (d) Drill hole at proper place in header and head jamb.

   (e) Anchor one end of pull wire at proper place on door and thread free end through holes.

   (f) Close door and attach pull wire to pull ring.

   (g) Arm and conceal boobytrap.

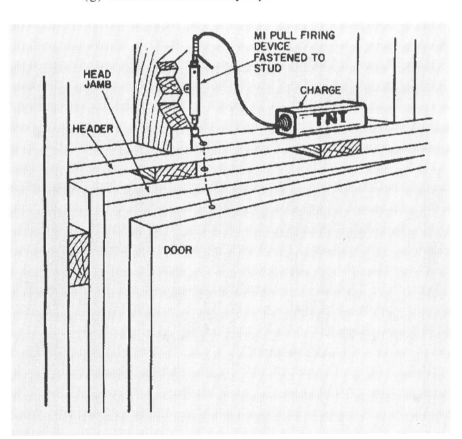

(2) *Side jamb rigging.*
(a) Attach metal brackets to side jamb close enough to wedge two flashlight batteries between.
(b) Insert sheet explosive charge snugly between stud and jamb.
(c) Place electric blasting cap in charge, and fasten one leg wire to top bracket
(d) Bore pull wire hole at proper spot inside jamb.
(e) Cut other leg wire long enough to twist on an insulated loop on one end and fit over pull wire hole. Loop should be about ^ inch in diameter.
(f) Twist on uninsulated loop on one end of leg wire and secure to lower bracket so that loop fits over pull wire hole. Fasten wire to jamb.
(g) Anchor one end of insulated pull wire at proper spot on door, and thread free end through pull wire hole and loop fastened to jamb.
(h) Close door. Fasten free end of pull wire to other loop to hold it snugly against stud.
(i) Check circuit with galvonometer first, then
(j) Install batteries between brackets.
(k) Conceal boobytrap.

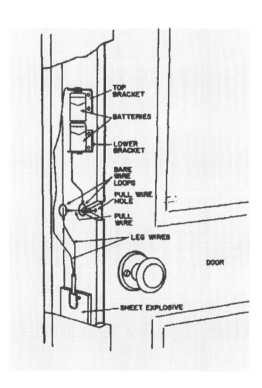

TOP BRACKET
BATTERIES
LOWER BRACKET
BARE WIRE LOOPS
PULL WIRE HOLE
PULL WIRE
LEG WIRES
DOOR
SHEET EXPLOSIVE

43. Structural Framework

a. In a building charges should be placed where detonation will seriously impair its structural strength, such as walls, chimneys, beams, and columns. Charges and firing devices must be carefully concealed to avoid detection.

b. In boobytrapping load-bearing walls, several charges should be laid to detonate simultaneously near the base. Chimneys and fireplaces are difficult to boobytrap for charges placed there are readily detected. These should detonate from intense heat.

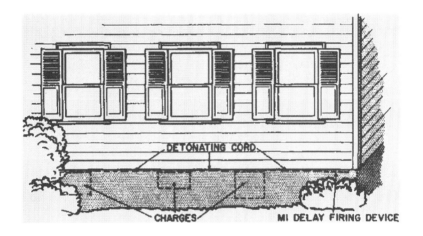

e. Beams and columns when they collapse cause much more damage than walls because they bear much more weight.

    (1) In wooden beams, holes for concealed explosives should be bored close enough together for sympathetic detonation. An Ml delay firing device and detonator placed in a hole within the bulk explosive charge should suffice. Buildings of masonry and steel construction may also be booby-trapped with delay charges. The difficulty of the job depends often on the interior finish, type of decoration, heating ducts, air conditioning, and type of floors.

    (2) A column may be destroyed by a charge buried below ground level at its base. Although heavy delay charges like these are often considered mines, they are shown here because they may be found in boobytrap locations.

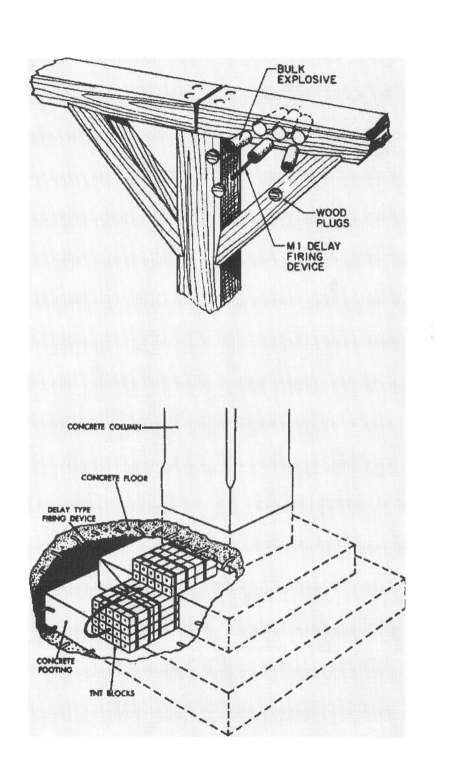

d. Loose floor boards sometimes are excellent objects for booby-trapping. The rigging must escape detection, however; otherwise, it will be ineffective. This rigging might be harder to detect if the support underneath is chiseled out to let the floorboard sink about 1/4 inch when tramped on.

e. A double delay chain detonating boobytrap should be very effective if timed right and skillfully laid. *First,* is the explosive of a minor charge laid in an upper story damaging the building only slightly. *Then,* after a curious crowd has gathered, a second heavy charge or series of charges go off, seriously damaging or destroying the building and killing or wounding many onlookers.

Vacated buildings provide much opportunity for boobytrapping. Hurriedly departing occupants usually leave behind such odds and ends as desks, filing cases, cooking utensils, table items, rugs, lamps, and furniture. Electric light and power fixtures are also exploitable.

a. *Desk.* Because of its construction a desk is easily boobytrapped. If carefully placed the rigging may be nondetectable and if properly constructed, cannot be neutralized. Electric firing systems are the most suitable for this purpose. Sheet explosive is much better than other types, because its adhesive surface holds it firmly in place. Check the circuit with a galvonometer *before* installing the batteries.

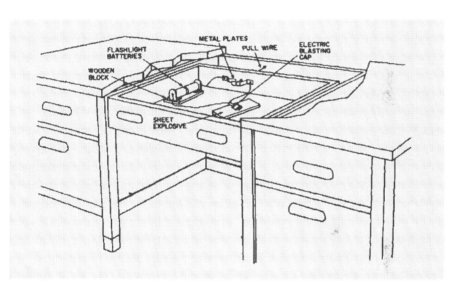

6. *Office Equipment.* Many items used in offices have boobytrap potential.

(1) *Telephone list finder.*
(a) Remove contents from finder.
(b) Assemble sheet explosive, shrapnel, and blasting cap.
(c) Remove insulation from ends of wires and twist to form loop switch.
(d) Place boobytrap in finder so that the raising of the lid draws the loops together.
(e) Insulate inside of case from contact with loops with friction tape.

(f) Check circuit with galvanometer *first,* then install batteries.

Note. Batteries may be connected to legwires by wrapping them tightly in place with friction tape.

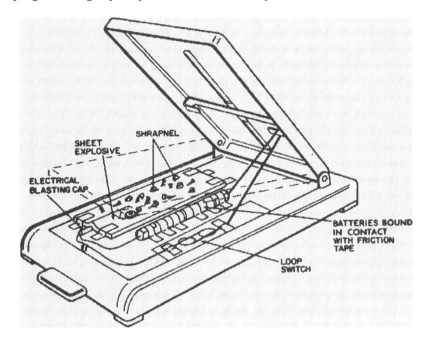

(2) *Card File.* A wooden card file can be boobytrapped effectively by the use of a mousetrap rigged as a trigger, a standard base with blasting cap attached, a support block fastened inside to hold the firing assembly at the proper level for operation, and a trigger block to hold the trigger in armed position.

  (a) Rig wire trigger of mousetrap with screw and metal strip.

  (b) Locate support block on strips at proper level to fix trigger in trigger block.

  (c) Bore hole in support block at proper place to admit standard base and blasting cap so that sheet metal screw will strike percussion cap.

  (d) Insert explosive, then support block with mousetrap, standard base, and blasting cap in position.

  (e) Raise trigger and close lid so that trigger is fixed in firing position.

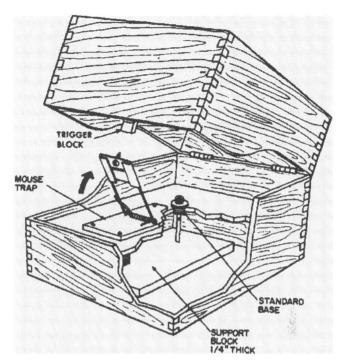

Electric Iron.

(1) Remove bottom plate.

(2) Insert bulk explosive and electric blasting cap.

(3) Attach shortened leg wires to power inlet.

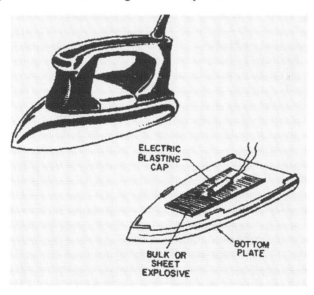

Teakettle.

(1) Assemble sheet explosive, electric blasting cap and mercury element in teakettle.

(2) Check circuit with galvanometer first, then install batteries.

Note. Batteries may be bound tightly in circuit with friction tape. For safety and ease of assembly, use a wrist watch delay in circuit (para 60d).

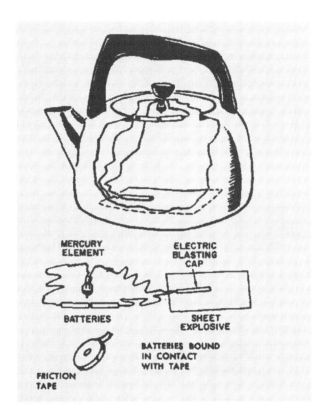

MERCURY
ELEMENT

ELECTRIC
BLASTING
CAP

BATTERIES

SHEET
EXPLOSIVE

BATTERIES BOUND
IN CONTACT
WITH TAPE

FRICTION
TAPE

e. *Pressure Cooker.*

(1) *Antidisturbance circuit.*

(a) Assemble sheet explosive, mercury element, and electric blasting cap in cooker.

(b) Check circuit with galvanometer *first,* then install batteries.

Note. Batteries may be bound-tightly in circuit with friction tape. For safety and ease of assembly, use a wrist watch delay in circuit (para *60d).*

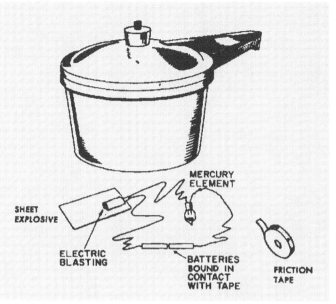

(2) *Loop switch.*

    (1) Assemble sheet explosive and electric blasting cap.

    (2) Cut leg wires to proper length. Remove insulation from ends and twist to form loop switch.

    (3) *Check circuit with galvonometer.*

    (4) Fasten one leg wire (insulated) to lid to serve as pull wire.

    (5) Secure batteries in circuit by wrapping tightly with friction tape.

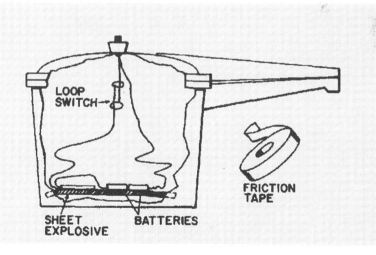

/. Radio and Television Sets. Both sets may be boobytraped by assembling a charge and an electric blasting cap inside the case. The leg wires are connected in the circuit for detonation at turning of off-on switch.

Extreme care is required in connecting leg wires to prevent premature explosion.

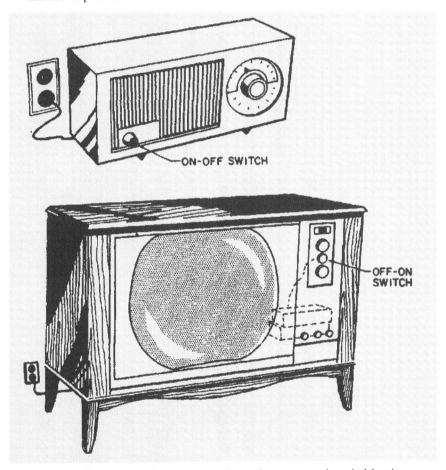

ON-OFF SWITCH

OFF-ON SWITCH

g. Bed. Two methods may be used—a charge, nonelectric blasting cap, and pull firing device or a charge, batteries, electric blasting cap, and a mercury switch element.

    (1) *Nonelectric rigging.*

        (a) Assemble pull wire, M1 pull firing device, blasting cap, and sheet explosive charge.

        (b) Anchor pull wire so that a person sitting or lying on bed will initiate firing device.

        (c) Conceal boobytrap.

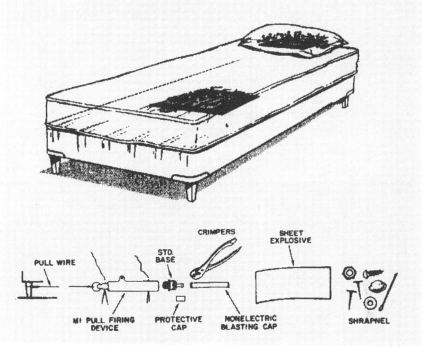

(2) *Electric rigging.*

    (a) Assemble sheet explosive charge, electric blasting cap, and mercury element.

    (b) Check circuit with galvanometer.

    (c) Place boobytrap on bed to initiate when its level position is disturbed.

    (d) Install batteries in circuit by wrapping tightly with friction tape.

    (e) Conceal boobytrap.

Note. For safety and ease of assembly, use a wrist watch delay in circuit (para 60d).

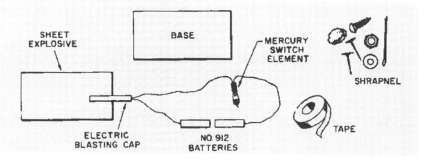

h. Chairs and Sofas. These may be boobytrapped nonelectrically and electrically as in / above. For nonelectric rigging the M1A1 pressure firing device, nonelectric blasting cap and sheet explosive charge are probably the most suitable. The sofa because of its size should have more than one rigging. If the electrical method is used *the circuit should be tested with the galvanometer before the batteries are installed.*

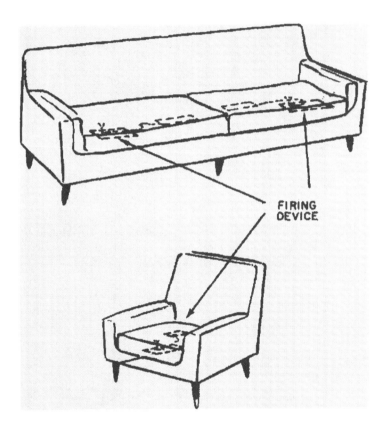

FIRING DEVICE

i. Book. A book with an attractive cover is sure to invite examination.
- (1) Cut hole in book large enough to accommodate the rigging.
- (2) Assemble sheet explosive, electric blasting cap, mercury element, and shrapnel.
- (3) *Test circuit with galvanometer first,* then
- (4) Secure batteries in circuit by wrapping tightly with friction tape.

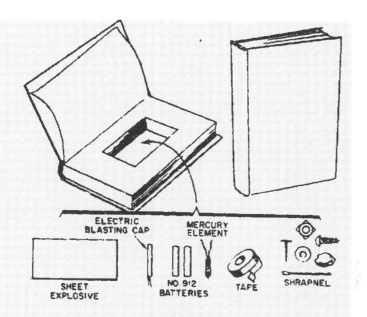

ELECTRIC
BLASTING CAP

MERCURY
ELEMENT

SHEET
EXPLOSIVE

NO. 9I2
BATTERIES

TAFE

SHRAPNEL

45. Highways, Trails, and Paths

Boobytraps used along roads are a great help in slowing down enemy traffic, especially if they are laid in and around other obstructions. Those placed on paths and trails are excellent against raiding parties that must operate under cover of darkness.

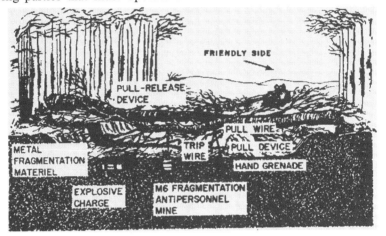

46. Locations

Boobytraps in roadway obstructions should be concealed on the enemy side. If the obstruction is heavy, requiring force to remove it, boobytraps concealed underneath will increase its effectiveness. Fragmentation charges are very destructive against personnel. These include hand grenades; bounding antipersonnel mines with their own special fuzes actuated by pressure or trip wire; ordinary explosive charges covered with pieces of scrap metal, nails, gravel, lengths of wire, nuts and bolts; and the like. The latter may be actuated by any of the standard firing devices—by pressure, pressure-release, pull-release, and pull.

    a. The jet of the M2A3 shaped charge from the roadside directed into a moving vehicle is very destructive.

        (1) Assemble an M3 pull-release firing device and detonator, *length of detonating cord, priming adapter, and non-electric* blasting cap.

        (2) Drive anchor stake in berm at side of road and attach pull wire. Drive stake or lay log, stone, or other object on other side to support pull wire at proper height off ground.

        (3) Attach firing device assembly to stake at proper position.

        (4) Fix shaped charge in position to direct explosive jet into vehicle when front wheels hit trip wire.

(5) Attach free end of pull wire in hole in winch and draw taut.
(6) Screw priming adapter and nonelectric blasting cap in threaded cap well.
(7) Conceal boobytrap.
(8) Arm firing device.

Note: Cone may be filled with fragments.

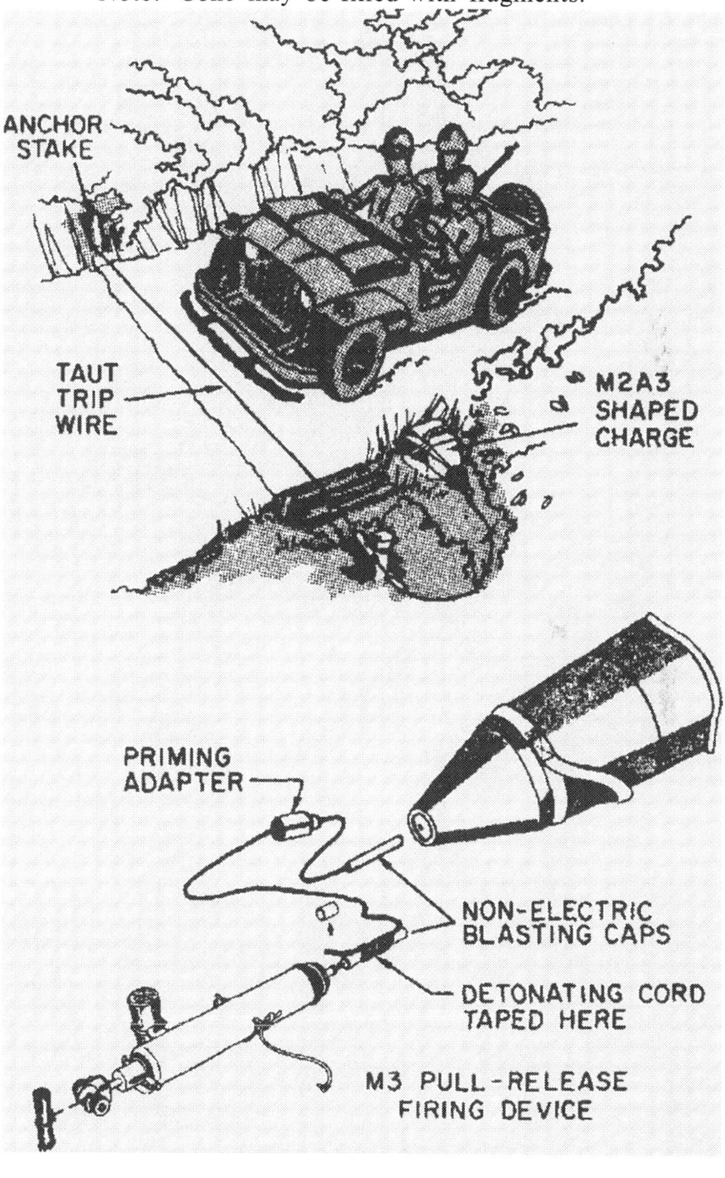

ANCHOR STAKE

TAUT TRIP WIRE

M2A3 SHAPED CHARGE

PRIMING ADAPTER

NON-ELECTRIC BLASTING CAPS

DETONATING CORD TAPED HERE

M3 PULL-RELEASE FIRING DEVICE

b. An M3 shaped charge boobytrap placed overhead in a tree in a wooded area will destroy both tank and crew if located properly. Trip wire, being very thin and camoufloage-colored, is not easily detected by a driver.

   (1) Assemble two firing devices (only one may be necessary) with detonators and lengths of detonating cord and a detonating cord primer.

   (2) Attach firing assemblies and M3 shaped charge in position in tree, so that when the vehicle contacts the trip wires, the explosive jet will penetrate the crew compartment.

   (3) Arm boobytrap.

c. Boobytraps laid in and along a narrow path may prove a delaying or frustrating obstacles to foot troops. These may be improvised shrapnel charges with a pressure-release firing device concealed under a stone, piece of wood, or other object, or with a pull or pull-release firing device and a trip wire. The latter would be very effective against patrols.

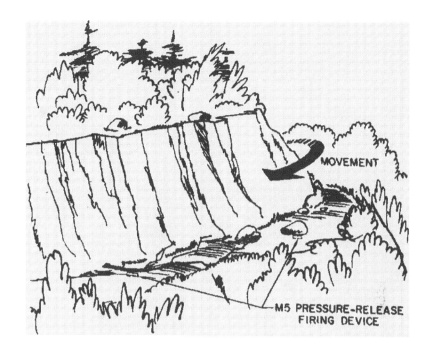

MOVEMENT

M5 PRESSURE-RELEASE FIRING DEVICE

47. Special Locations

a. Abandoned serviceable or repairable items are frequently boobytrapped if time and equipment are available. Even unserviceable items may be rigged against scavangers who may search through the wreckage for useful things.

b. Abandoned ammunition should be exploited to the maximum. Chain detonations of connected mines or sections of bangalore torpedo are particularly effective.

c. Boobytraps are applicable to storage areas where materials cannot be removed or destroyed. Several charges strategically laid will prove very rewarding. A lumber pile provides excellent concealment for an explosive rigging. Sheet explosive may be used in many places where TNT is impractical, because of its size and shape. Here again chain detonations of explosive blocks and bangalore torpedos will do extensive damage, if the firing mechanism is properly located and cunningly concealed.

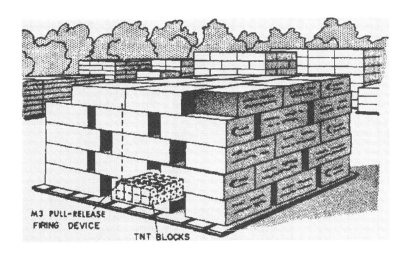

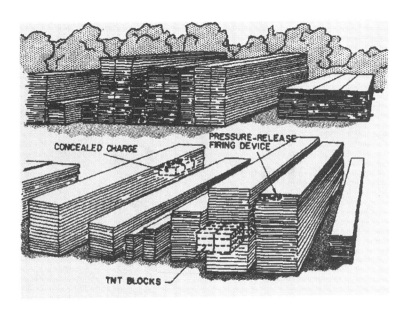

43. Abandoned Vehicles
   a. Truck Wheel.

   (1) Insert length of heavy wire in interceptor hole in firing device.
   (2) Remove safety pin and replace with length of thin wire. Bend both wires slightly to prevent falling out.
   (3) Assemble standard base, nonelectric blasting cap, and firing device.
   (4) Assemble two 2-block explosive charges, nonelectric blasting caps, priming adapters, and length of detonating cord.
   (5) In hole prepared under truck wheel, assemble bearing blocks (take weight off explosive charge), charges, bearing board, protective blocks (take weight off firing device), and firing device.
   (6) Arm firing device.
   (7) Cover boobytrap, and camouflage.

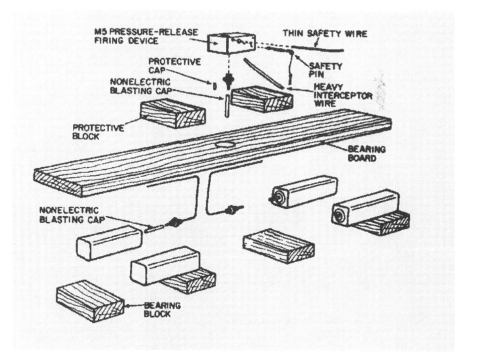

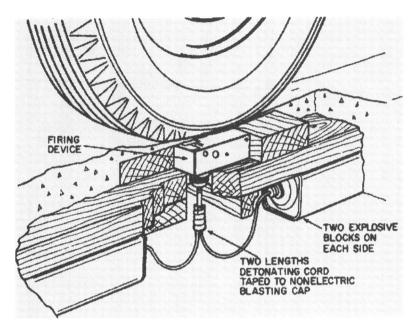

FIRING
DEVICE

TWO EXPLOSIVE
BLOCKS ON
EACH SIDE

TWO LENGTHS
DETONATING CORD
TAPED TO NONELECTRIC
BLASTING CAP

b. Motor. The fan belt is an excellent anchor for a pull wire. The pull wire will be much harder to detect if anchored underneath the bottom pulley, from where it may be extended any length to the firing device and charge.

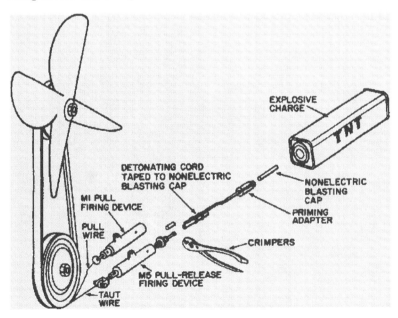

EXPLOSIVE
CHARGE

DETONATING CORD
TAPED TO NONELECTRIC
BLASTING CAP

NONELECTRIC
BLASTING
CAP

M1 PULL
FIRING DEVICE

PRIMING
ADAPTER

PULL
WIRE

CRIMPERS

M5 PULL-RELEASE
FIRING DEVICE

TAUT
WIRE

c. Electric System. A useful combination is a charge primed with an electric blasting cap with clamps attached to the leg wires. This may be attached to detonate by turning on the ignition switch, engaging the starter, braking, and the like.

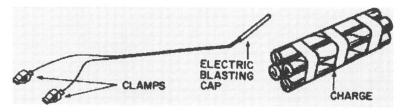

d. Body. Another combination useful in rigging a seat or any other part of the vehicle body is a charge detonated electrically by means of a mercury switch element.

    (1) Assemble charge, electric blasting cap, and mercury element.

    (2) Place boobytrap in position and check circuit with a galvanometer.

    (3) Attach batteries in circuit by wrapping tightly with friction tape.

Note. Always check circuit before attaching batteries.

This rigging may be assembled in a small package for use in a seat cushion or separated for convenience for another location in the body of the vehicle.

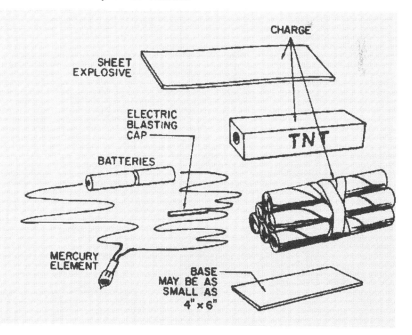

CHAPTER 5

MISCELLANEOUS BOOBYTRAPS

Section I. STANDARD BOOBYTRAPS

49. Tactical Use

In World War II, every major power manufactured boobytraps to use against the enemy. Most of them were charged imitations of useful objects, which maimed or killed helpless soldiers that handled them. The defect common to all standard boobytraps however, is that after the first or second explosion, all others of the same type become ineffective. A "one-shot" job hardly justifies production costs.

50. Foreign Types

a. The Soviets used more standard boobytraps in World War II than any other combatant. A weird assortment of charged imitations of items issued to German soldiers were dropped from Soviet planes. Some of these were:

(1) Cartridge boxes, apparently filled with ammunition, containing high explosives and detonators.

(2) Bandage packets containing detonators and shrapnel.

(3) Bandage cases with Red Cross insignia rigged as mines.

(4) Rubber balls, about twice the size of a fist that detonated upon impact.

(5) Silver-grey light metal boxes or Masks that exploded when the lid was raised.

(6) Cognac bottles filled with incendiary liquid.

(7) Small red flags marked with an M and attached to mines that detonated when the flag was removed.

(8) Imitation earth-grey colored frogs that detonated when pressed on.

(9) Flashlights containing high explosive which detonated when the switch was moved.

(10) Mechanical pencils, watches, cigarette cases, cigarette lighters, salt cellars, and similar items that detonated when handled.

b. Knowing the German interest in books, the Soviets prepared a book boobytrap. The charge inside detonated when the cover was raised.

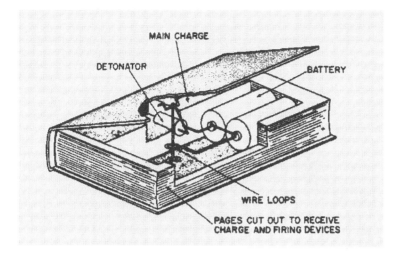

MAIN CHARGE

DETONATOR

BATTERY

WIRE LOOPS

PAGES CUT OUT TO RECEIVE
CHARGE AND FIRING DEVICES

c. The British also had a book boobytrap; but it was slightly more complicated than the Soviet version, above.

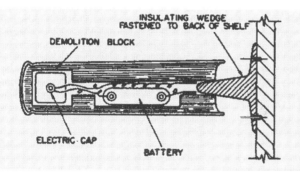

INSULATING WEDGE
FASTENED TO BACK OF SHELF

DEMOLITION BLOCK

ELECTRIC CAP

BATTERY

d. All sorts of dirty-trick devices were used by the enemy.
   (1) A flashlight was rigged with a charge and an electric detonator powered and actuated by the original dry cell battery switch, and circuit.

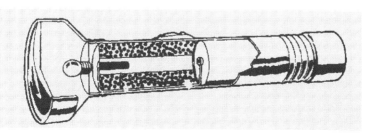

(2) Bottles designed to look like liquor bottles were filled with a liquid explosive detonated by a pull-friction fuze attached to the cork.

(3) A fountain pen, though very small, was rigged with an explosive charge, a spring driven striker to fire a percussion cap, and a detonator.

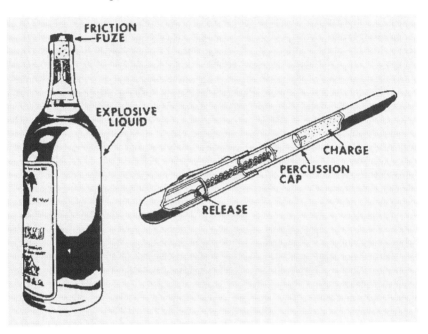

(4) The Japanese manufactured a pipe boobytrap with a charge, detonator, and spring-loaded striker.

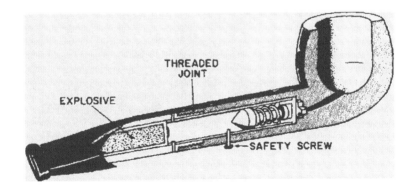

(5) The Italians had a boobytrapped headset containing an electric detonator connected to the terminals on the back. The connection of the headset into the live communication line initiated detonation.

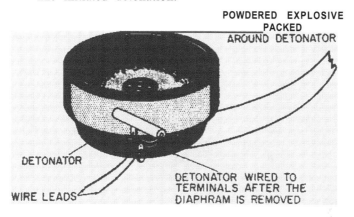

POWDERED EXPLOSIVE PACKED AROUND DETONATOR

DETONATOR

WIRE LEADS

DETONATOR WIRED TO TERMINALS AFTER THE DIAPHRAM IS REMOVED

(6) The Germans converted their own and enemy standard canteens into boobytraps. The explosive charge was detonated by a pull fuze and a pull wire connected to the cap. When partially filled with water and placed in its canvas case, it was very deceptive. The canteen booby-trap had an effective radius of 3 to 5 yards.

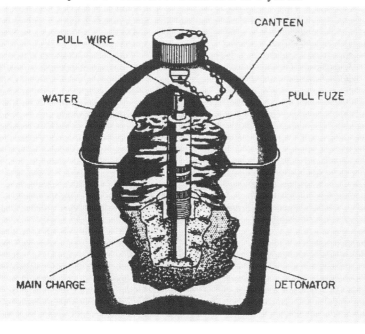

PULL WIRE

CANTEEN

WATER

PULL FUZE

MAIN CHARGE

DETONATOR

(7) Another German device was the boobytrap whistle. This consisted of a policeman's or referee's whistle with a charge and a metal ball covered with a layer of friction compound. Blowing the whistle moved the ball, igniting the friction compound and detonating the charge.

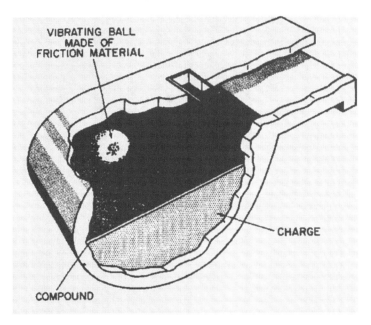

(8) The German Peters candy bar boobytrap was ingenious indeed. The explosive charge, fuze, and thin canvas pull device were covered with chocolate.

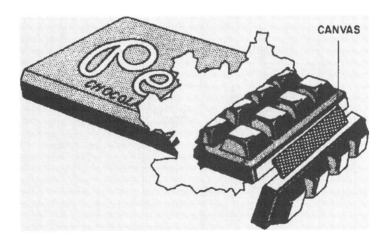

51. Ingenuity

a. Through information on military operations in World War II, the U.S. soldier has been well-prepared for the dangerous mission of laying, detecting, and disarming boobytraps in conventional warfare. However, he now is virtually a novice in comparison with the cunning and ingenious present day guerrilla, who at the start was almost totally lacking in material and equipment.

b. Experience has shown that in guerrilla warfare, carried on by illy-equipped native populations, boobytrapping success depends largely on ingenuity. Explosive, a necessary element, is either improvised from commercial ingredients or captured from the enemy. Captured mines, ammunition, and other similar material are disassembled and every ounce of explosive saved.

52. Training

Every soldier should have some training in the lessons learned from the guerrillas, for many items they have improvised and the way they have used them are also applicable to conventional warfare. With little effort, a soldier may be trained so that with no military equipment whatever but with ample funds, he may prepare himself to fight effectively with materials available from merchants, junk piles, and salvage.

53. Application

The improvisations included in this section are gathered from numerous sources. Some may have wider application to boobytrapping than others. How the guerrilla may use them, however, is unpredictable. All are presented to stimulate initiative and arouse enthusiasm to out-do backward enemy peoples in devising and placing boobytraps and to develop a higher level of proficiency than ever before in their detection and removal.

54. Improvised Time Fuze and Explosive Caps

a. Fast burning fuse (UO inches per minute).

(1) Braid three lengths of cotton string together.

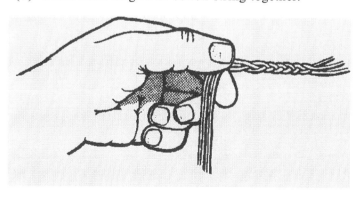

(2) Moisten fine black powder to form a paste. Rub paste into twisted string with fingers and allow to dry. If a powder is not available, mix 25 parts potassium nitrate (saltpeter) in an equal amount of water and add 3 parts pulverized charcoal and 2 parts pulverized sulphur to form a paste. Rub paste into twisted string and allow to dry.

(8) Check burning rate before using.

b. Slow burning fuse (2 inches per minute).

(1) Wash three lengths of string or three shoelaces in hot soapy water and rinse.
(2) Dissolve 1 part potassium nitrate or potassium chlorate and 1 part granulated sugar in 2 parts hot water.
(3) Soak string or shoelaces in solution and braid three strands together. Allow to dry.
(4) Check burning rate.
(5) Before using, coat several inches of the end to be inserted into cap or material to be ignited with black powder paste (a (2) above).

c. Electric Blasting Cap.

(1) With file or other instrument make hole in end of light bulb.
(2) If jacket is not available, solder or securely fasten two wires to bulb—one on metal threads at side and other at metal contact on bottom.
(3) Fill bulb and empty portion of blasting cap with black powder. Tape blasting cap on top of bulb.

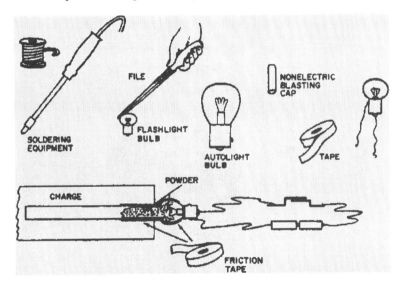

d. Percussion Cap Assembly.

   (1) Remove projectile, but not powder, from small arms cartridge.

   (2) Tape nonelectric blasting cap securely in cartridge.

55. Pull Firing Devices

   a. Tube and Striker.

Assemble tube, spring, striker shaft with hole or with hex nut, soft wood or metal top plug, pull pin, and improvised percussion cap assembly.

Note. Always assemble firing device before attaching the improvised percussion cap assembly.

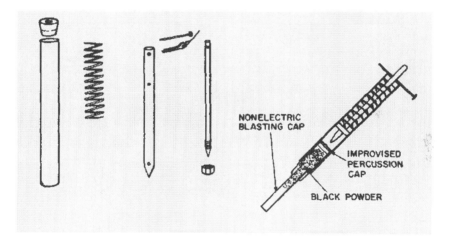

   b. Clothes Pin.

   (1) Wrap stripped ends of leg wires around clothes pin jaws to make electrical contact.

   (2) Assemble charge, adapter, electric blasting cap, and clothes pin.

   (3) Insert wooden wedge, anchor clothes pin, and install trip wire.

   (4) Check circuit with galvonometer *first,* then connect batteries.

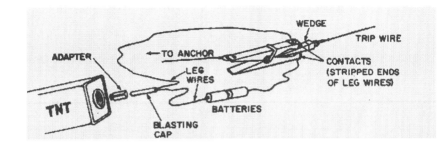

c. Stake or Pole Initiator.

(1) Assemble stake or pole, container, metal contact plates, charge, electric blasting cap, and pull cord.

(2) Check circuit with galvonometer *first,* then connect batteries.

(3) Fasten down top of container and seal hole around stake with friction tape.

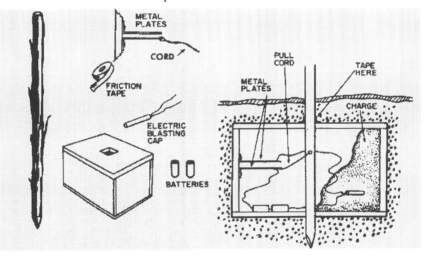

d. Rope and Cylinder.

(1) Cut leg wires to proper length.

(2) Prepare wooden end plugs and bore hole in one to receive leg wires.

(3) Thread leg wires through hole in block.

(4) Strip end of one leg wire and twist into loop, and secure other leg wire in position.

(5) Test circuit with galvonometer.

(6) Assemble metal cylinder, contact bolt, pull cord, charge, blasting cap, end blocks, and batteries.

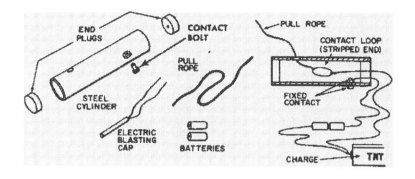

e. *Trip Lever and Putt Pin.*

(1) *Flat placement.*
Assemble container, charge, improvised pull firing device
(o above) and trip lever.

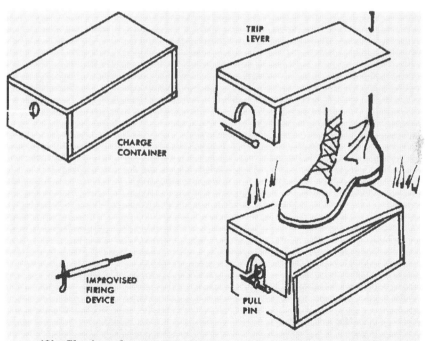

(2) *Sloping placement.*
Assemble container, charge, improvised firing device
(*a* above) and stake.

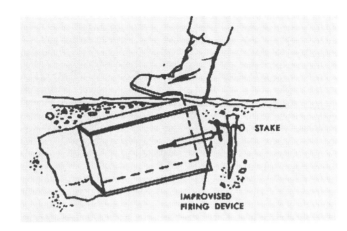

STAKE

IMPROVISED
FIRING DEVICE

56. Pressure Firing, Devices

a. Mechanical Concussion.

(1) Force striker into hole in pressure board.

(2) Insert wood or soft metal shear pin in shear pin hole.

(3) Assemble striker, metal tube, and improvised blasting cap (para 54).

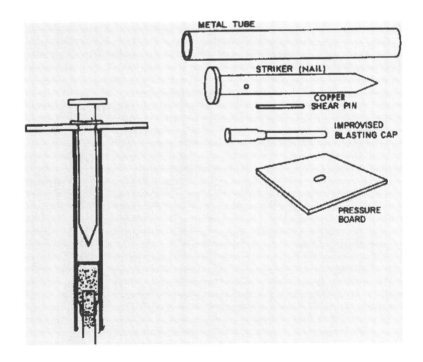

METAL TUBE

STRIKER (NAIL)

COPPER
SHEAR PIN

IMPROVISED
BLASTING CAP

PRESSURE
BOARD

6. *Electrical.*

  (1) *Lever arm.*

    (a) Attach contact blocks to ends of wooden levers.

    (b) Assemble wooden levers, rubber strip, and plastic sponge.

    (c) Attach leg wire contacts.

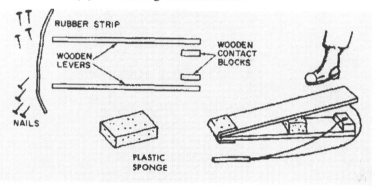

  (2) *Flexible side.*

    (a) Attach metal contact plates to bearing boards.

    (b) Thread leg wires through holes in lower bearing board and attach to contact plates.

    (c) Attach flexible sides.

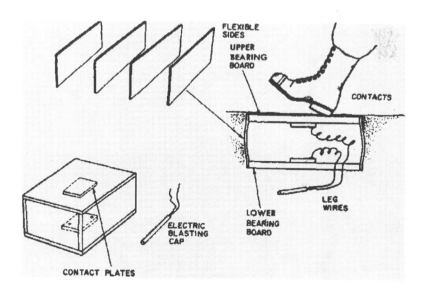

(8) *Springed pressure board.*

    (a) Assemble metal contacts, springs, bearing board, and pressure board.

    (b) Attach leg wires to metal contacts.

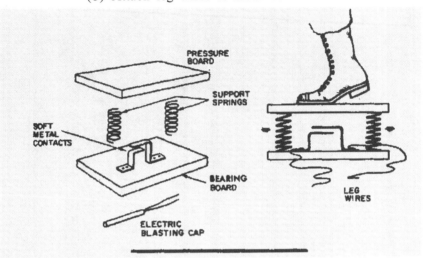

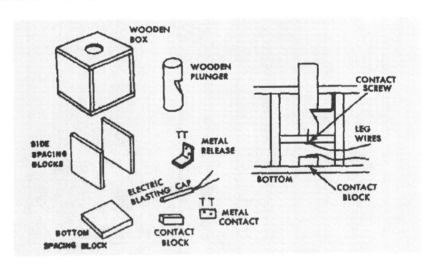

    (4) *Wooden plunger.*

        (a) Assemble box, leaving one side open.

        (b) Assemble contact plate and three spacing blocks inside box.

        (c) Drill holes in spacing block for leg wires.

(d) Assemble plunger, metal release, contact block, metal contact, and contact screw.

(e) Thread leg wire through holes in spacing block and attach to contacts.

(5) *Metal box.*

(a) Attach metal contact to wooden contact block.

(b) Assemble contact block and metal contact, brackets, metal release, plunger, and wooden box lid.

(c) Bore hole in side of box for leg wires.

(d) Thread leg wires through hole in box.

(e) Attach one leg wire to plunger, the other to metal contact.

Note. Batteries may be placed inside box if necessary.

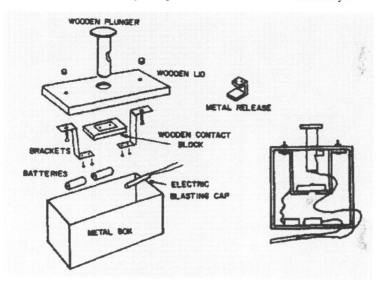

57. Tension-Release Bring Device

Attach stripped ends of circuit wires to ends of clothes pin to form contacts. Attach taut trip wires below contacts.

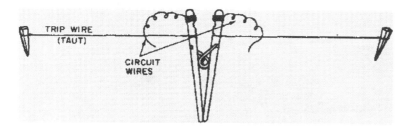

58. rVcawrt-RcJMM
   a. *Double Contact.*
   (1) Bore holes in top of mine body to accommodate long contacts.
   (2) Assemble pressure board, coil springs, wooden contact board and metal contacts.
   (3) Attach circuit wires.

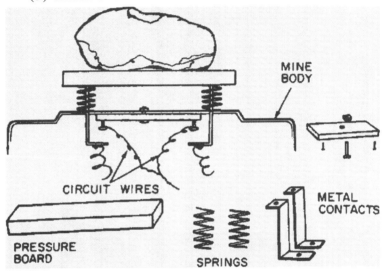

b. *Clothes Pin.*
   (1) Attach stripped ends of circuit wires to clothes pin to make contacts.
   (2) Place mine on top, keeping contacts apart.

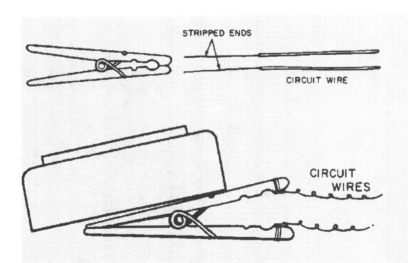

c. *Bottom Plunger.*

(1) Bore hole in bottom of nune case to admit plunger.
(2) Attach lower metal contact over hole.
(3) Assemble mine, pressure block, upper metal contact, and nonmetallic plunger.
(4) Attach circuit wires.

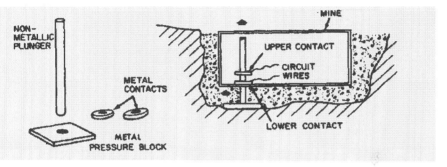

d. *Mousetrap.*

(1) *Mechanical*
   See para 44 *b* (2)
(2) *Electrical*
   (a) Remove triggering devices from mousetrap.
   (b) Assemble trap, contact plate, and circuit wires.
   (c) Place weight on top with striker in armed position.

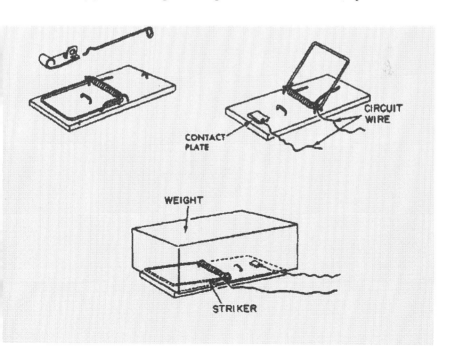

59. Anti-Lift Devices

a. Loop Contact.

(1) Drill hole in bottom of mine to admit insulated pull wire.

(2) Assemble plunger, metal release, and contact plate.

(S) Attach circuit wires and bare loop to plunger contact and contact plate.

(4) Thread anchored insulated trip wire through holes in bottom of mine and contact plate and attach to bare loop.

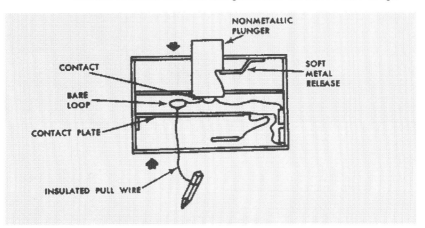

b. Double Detonator.

(1) Drill three holes—one in bottom, one in partition, and one in side—to admit nonmetallic plunger and two electric blasting caps.

(2) Assemble blasting cap, leg wires, contact plates, plunger and pressure block.

(3) *Check circuit with galvonometer first.* Then connect batteries with friction tape.

(4) Install blasting cap connected to pressure firing device in side of mine.

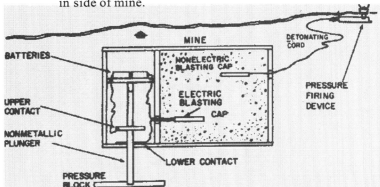

c. *Sliding Contact.*
 (1) Assemble metal cap, nonmetallic tube or carton, sliding contact, wooden plug, and leg wires at contacts.
 (2) *Check circuit with a galvonometer first,* then connect batteries with friction tape.
 (3) Install assembly in tube.

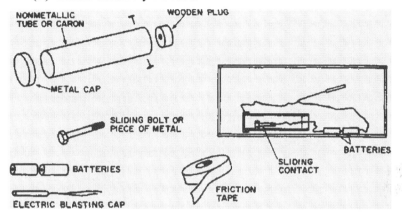

60. Delay firing Devices
 a. *Cigarette Timer.*
 (1) Test burning rate of time fuze and cigarette. (A cigarette usually burns at the rate of 1 inch in 7 to 8 minutes.)
 (2) Cut sloping end on length of time fuze.
 (3) Assemble sloped end of time fuze, match head, and cigarette.

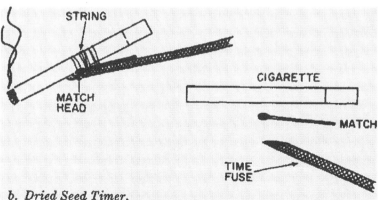

b. *Dried Seed Timer.*
 (1) Determine expansion rate of seeds.
 (2) Place in jar and add water.
 (3) Assemble jar, lid, circuit wires, metal contacts, and metal disk and secure with friction tape.

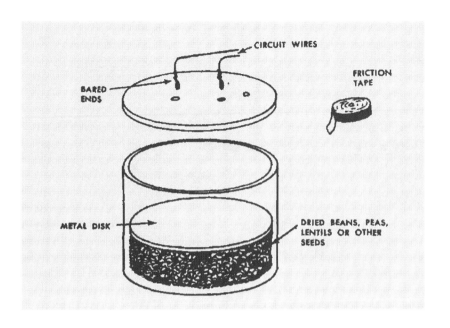

c. *Alarm Clock Timers.*
    (1) *Electric.*
        (a) Assemble base, metal contacts, and alarm clock.
        (b) Tie knot in one end of string. Thread other end through metal contacts and attach to alarm winding stem, which winches string and closes circuit.

Note. An alarm clock, being a very versatile delay, may be connected in many other ways.

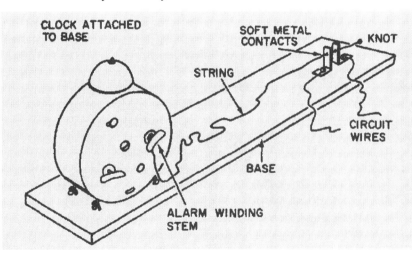

(2) *Nonelectric.*

    (a) Drill hole in board of proper size to hold standard base tightly.

    (b) Remove standard safety pin from firing device and replace with easily removed pin.

    (c) Remove protective cap from standard base and crimp on nonelectric blasting cap.

    (d) Screw standard base with blasting cap into firing device.

    (e) Assemble alarm clock and firing device on board.

    (f) Attach one end of length of string to eye in safety pin and the .other to alarm winding stem, which winches string and removes safety pin.

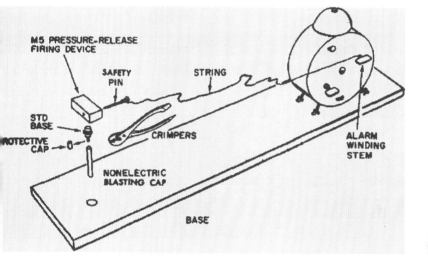

d. Wrist Watch Timer.

  (1) *One-hour delay or less.*

    (a) Drill small hole in plastic crystal and attach circuit wire with screw of proper length to contact minute hand.

    (b) Attach other circuit wire to case.

  (2) *Twelve-hour delay or less.*

    (a) Remove minute hand.

    (b) Drill small hole in plastic crystal and attach circuit wire with screw of proper length to contact hour hand.

    (c) Attach other circuit wire to case.

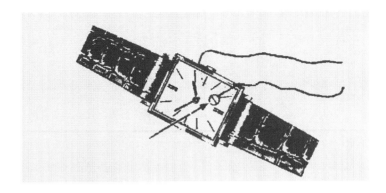

61. Bombs

  a. Pipe Bombs.

    (1) *Grenade.*

      (a) Drill hole in cap or plug to admit length of time fuze.

      (b) Crimp nonelectric blasting cap to length of time fuze.

      (c) Assemble pipe, caps or plugs, time fuze primer, and explosive charge.

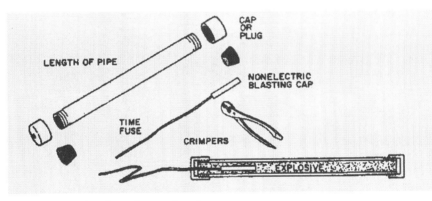

    (2) *Antidisturbanee bomb.*

      (a) Drill hole in end cap to admit length of burnt time fuze to make a bomb look like a "dud."

      (b) Attach electric cap and mercury element on base.

      (c) Test circuit with galvonometer *first,* then connect batteries with friction tape.

      (d) Assemble bomb.

Caution: If possible, assemble bomb *in place,* as the mercury element, when disturbed, may cause premature explosion. To assemble more safely and easily, attach wrist watch timer in circuit.

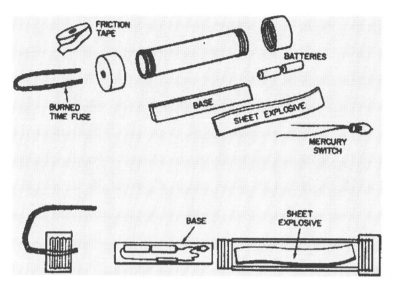

(3) *Shotgun bomb.*

    (a) Close one end of pipe with hammer, allowing open-
-ing for detonating cord primer or electric blasting
cap.

    (b) Remove protective cap from M1A1 pressure or M1
pull firing device and crimp on nonelectric blasting
cap.

    (c) Screw standard base with blasting cap into firing
device.

    (d) Assemble pipe, shrapnel, wadding, explosive, non-
electric primer or electric blasting cap (for controlled firing), and proper firing device.

Note. The force of the explosive and the strength of the pipe are
important in calculating the size of the charge.

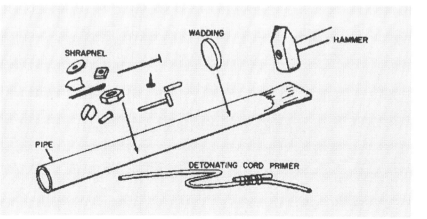

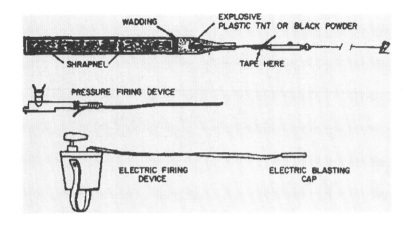

b. *Nail Grenade.*

Attach nails to top and sides of charge by means of tape or string. Under certain conditions, nails may be required on only two sides, or even on one side.

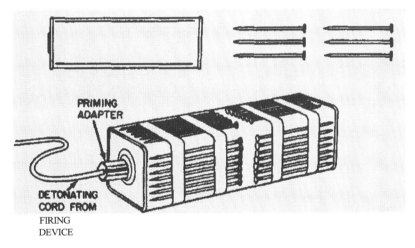

c. *Delay Bomb.*

    (1) *Chemical delay.*

        (a) Crimp nonelectric blasting cap on base of appropriate M1 delay firing device.

        (b) Assemble firing device and charge in package.

        (c) Crush copper end of firing device with fingers.

        (d) Place package in suitcase or container.

Note. Use this bomb only when delay is necessary but accuracy is secondary, as the delay time of any chemical firing device varies considerably according to temperature.

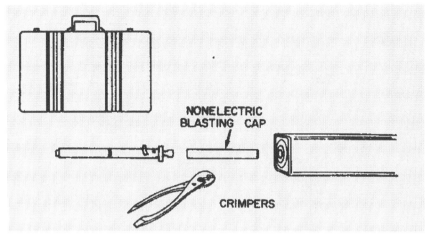

(2) *Alarm clock delay.*

    (a) Drill hole in wooden base of proper size to hold standard base firmly.

    (b) Remove standard safety pin from M5 pressure-release firing device and replace with easily-removed pin.

    (c) Crimp nonelectric blasting cap on standard base and attach to firing device.

    (d) Assemble alarm clock and firing device on wooden base.

    (e) Attach one end of string in eye in pull pin and the other to the alarm winding stem so that its turning will winch the string and withdraw the pin.

    (f) Place assembly in suitcase or container.

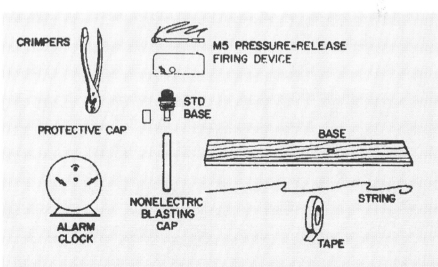

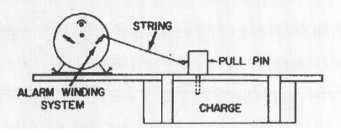

d. *Envelope Bomb.*

(1) Cut leg wires of electric blasting cap of proper length to make circuit.

(2) Strip insulation off ends of circuit wires and twist into 14,-inch loops to make loop switch.

(3) Test circuit with galvonometer *first,* then attach batteries.

(4) Assemble cardboard base, batteries, electric blasting cap, and explosive as package.

(5) Attach one end of string to loop switch so that it will pull the bared loops together to close circuit.

(6) Cut hole inside of envelope under flap.

(7) Fix package in envelope firmly and thread string through hole.

(8) Attach string firmly but concealed to underside of flap.

(9) Close envelope with elastic band.

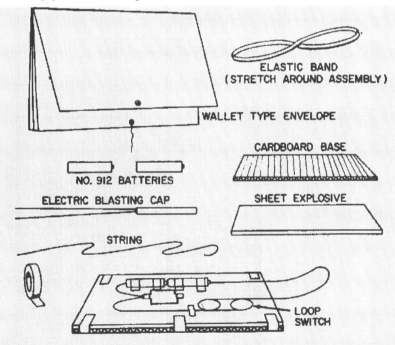

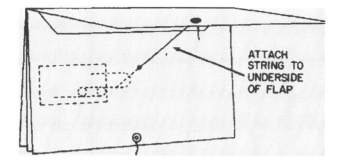

ATTACH STRING TO UNDERSIDE OF FLAP

e. Hot Shrapnel Bomb.
(1) Remove protective cap from standard base and crimp on nonelectric blasting cap.
(2) Screw base with cap in Ml pull firing device.
(3) Crimp nonelectric blasting cap on one end of length of detonating cord, and install in Claymore mine.
(4) Attach firing device to detonating cord with tape.
(5) Assemble Claymore mine with priming and firing accessories and drum of napalm.
(6) Arm firing device.

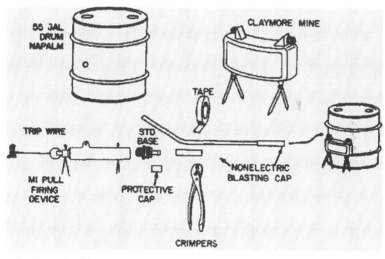

/. Rice Paddy Bomb.
(1) Remove protective cap from standard base and crimp on nonelectric blasting cap.
(2) Screw standard base with cap into Ml pull firing device.
(3) Assemble firing device, detonating cord, priming adapter, nonelectric blasting cap, and explosive charge.
(4) Attach charge to drum of napalm.
(5) Arm firing device.

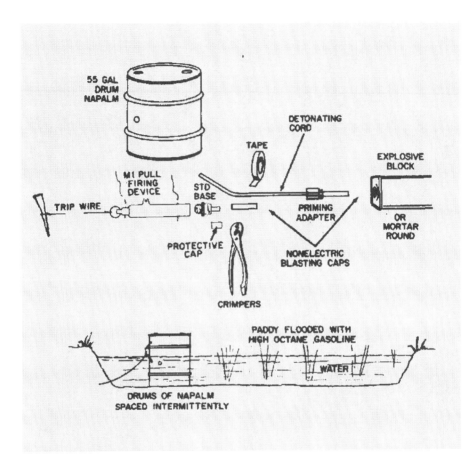

g. *Tin Can Bomb.*
  (1) Cut a notched metal contact disk to provide clearance for length of stiff insulated wire and **Vi** to **14** in. from walls of can.
  (2) Cut stiff insulated wire of proper length to support disk and strip insulation from both ends. Bend hook on one end to hold bare suspension wire.
  (3) Bend stiff wire to proper shape.
  (4) Assemble can, explosive, contact to can, blasting cap, insulated support wire, suspension wire and contact disk.
  (5) Check circuit with galvonometer *first,* then connect batteries.

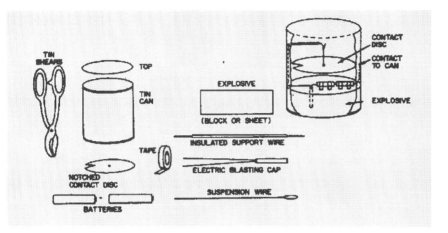

62. Miscellaneous Charges

 a. *Improvised Shaped Charge.*

   (1) Cut strip of thin metal to make cone of 30° to 60° angle
       to fit snugly into container.
   (2) Place cone in container.
   (3) Pack explosive firmly in container to a level of 2x height.
   (4) Attach standoffs to set charge above target at height of
       of cone.
       2x diameter of cone.
   (5) Attach blasting cap at rear dead center of charge.

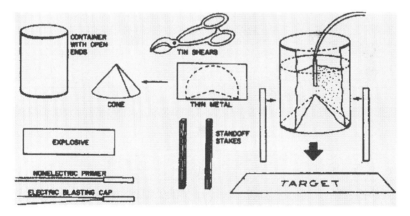

 6. *Improvised Antipersonnel Mine.*

   (1) Assemble container, explosive, separator, and shrapnel.
       *Explosive must be packed to uniform density and thick-
       ness* (should be Vi weight of shrapnel).
   (2) Remove protective cap from standard base and crimp on
       nonelectric blasting cap.

(3) Screw standard base with blasting cap into proper firing device.

(4) Secure firing device in'place.

(5) Fix primer in rear center of explosive and tape to firing device.

(6) Arm firing device.

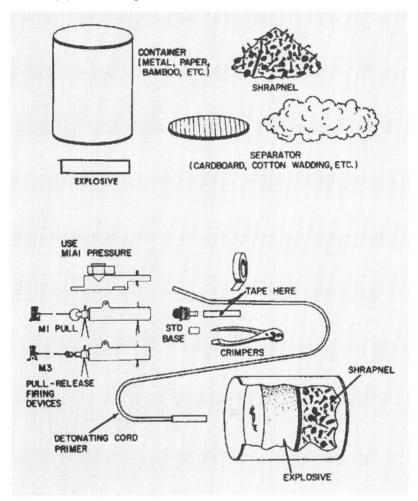

e. Platter Charge.

(1) Assemble container, charge, and platter. .Charge should weigh same as platter.

(2) Place primer in rear center of charge.

(3) Align center of platter with center of target mass.

(4) Attach and arm firing device.

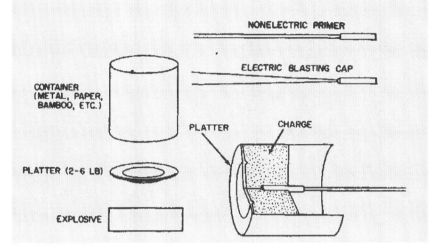

d. *Improvised Claymore.*

    (1) Attach shrapnel to *convex* side of base and cover with cloth, tape, or screen retainer.

    (2) Place layer of plastic explosive on *concave* side of base.

    (3) Attach legs to *concave* side of base.

    (4) Attach electric blasting cap at exact rear center.

    (5) Attach firing device to firing wires at proper distance from mine for safety.

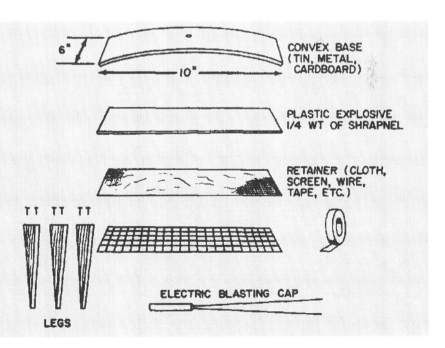

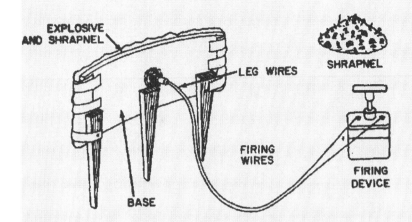

CHAPTER 6

BOOBYTRAP DETECTION AND REMOVAL

Section I. CLEARING METHODS

63. Technicians

a. Although engineer and infantry specialists are responsible for boobytrap detection and removal, all military organizations assigned to combat zone missions must provide trained men to assist them.

b. If possible, trained engineer, infantry, or explosive ordnance disposal units will search out and neutralize all boobytraps in front of friendly troops or prepare safe passage lanes. When discovered, boobytraps will either be disarmed immediately or marked by warning signs. Only the simple ones will be disarmed during attack. Those more complicated will be marked and reported for removal.

c. To avoid casualty, boobytrapped areas, especially villages and other inhabited places, should be bypassed, to be cleared by specialists later. Tactical units will neutralize boobytraps only when necessary for continued movement or operation.

64. Clearance Teams

Men who clear boobytraps are organized into disposal teams and assigned to specific areas according to their training and experience.

a. Direction and control is the responsibility of the person in charge of clearance activities, who will-
  (1) Maintain a control point near at hand and remain in close contact with his clearance parties.
  (2) Give assistance to disposal teams when required.
  (3) Preserve new types of enemy equipment found for more careful examination by engineer intelligence teams.

b. Searching parties will be sufficient in number to cover an area promptly, without interfering with each other.

c. In clearing a building, one person will direct all searching parties assigned.

d. Open area clearance will be preceded by reconnaissance if the presence of boobytraps is suspected. Once boobytraps are found, search must be thorough.

e. Searching parties must be rested frequently. A tired man, or one whose attention is attracted elsewhere, is a danger to himself and others working with him.

65. Tools and Equipment

a. *Body Armor.* Armor of various kinds is available. Special boots and shoe pacs, also issued, will give greater protection against blast than boots generally worn.

b. Mine Detectors.

(1) Three mine detectors useful in the removal of boobytraps are issued: AN/PRS-3 (Polly Smith) and the transistorized, aural indication model, designed for metal detection, and AN/PRS-4 for nonmetallic detection. Of the metal detectors, the transistorized model is the lighter and more powerful. All three models have the same deficiences. They may signal a small piece of scrap as well as a metal-cased explosive or signal an air pocket in the soil, a root, or disturbed soil generally.

(2) Operating time should not exceed 20 minutes to avoid operator fatigue. *Tired operators often become careless operators.*

c. Grapnels. These are hooks attached to a length of stout cord or wire, long enough for the operator jo pull a mine or boobytrap from place from a safe distance or from at least 50 meters behind cover.

d. Probes. Lengths of metal rod or stiff wire, or bayonets, are good probes for locating buried charges. Searching parties sometimes work with rolled-up sleeves better to feel trip wires and hidden objects.

e. Markers. Standard markers are carried by disposal teams to designate the location of known boobytraps, pending their removal.

f. Tape. Marking tape is useful for tracing safe routes and identifying dangerous areas.

g. Hand Tools. Small items, such as nails, cotter pins, pieces of wire, friction tape, safety pins, pliers, pocket knife, hand mirror, scissors, flashlight, and screw driver are very useful in boobytrap clearance.

66. Detection

a. The most careful observation is required for the detection of boobytraps. Soldiers must be trained and disciplined to be on guard, especially when moving over an area previously held by **the** enemy. Although a soldier may not be assigned the responsibility for their detection and clearance, he must be alert for any sign that **may** indicate their presence. He must also discipline himself to look carefully for concealed boobytraps before performing many **Acts** of normal life.

b. Often prisoners of war through interrogation give information on new or unknown boobytrap devices that may aid in their identification and handling later on. Local inhabitants also often provide information on boobytraps laid in the neighborhood.

e. Searching for boobytraps and delayed charges is difficult and tedious, particularly when intelligence is lacking or inadequate. The extent of search required, the **ease** of placing and camouflaging, and the great number of devices available to the enemy make the clearance of all charges almost impossible. Searching parties, before being sent out, will be briefed on all **that** is known about enemy activities in the area.

67. Outdoor Searching Techniques

As boobytraps are so deadly and as a rule cunningly conceived and hidden, outdoor searching parties should be suspicious of -

a. All moveable and apparently valuable and useful property.

b. All disturbed ground and litter from explosive containers.

e. Marks intentionally left behind to attract or divert attention.

d. Evidence of former camouflage.

e. Abrupt changes or breaks in the continuity of any object, such as unnatural appearances of fences, paint, vegetation, and dust.

f. Unnecessary things like nails, wire, or cord that may be part of a boobytrap.

g. Unusual marks that may be an enemy warning of danger.

h. All obstructions, for they are ideal spots for boobytraps. Search carefully before lifting a stone, moving a low hanging limb, or pushing aside a broken-down wheelbarrow.

i. Queer imprints or marks on a road, which may lead a curious person to danger.

j. Abandoned vehicles, dugouts, wells, machinery, bridges, gullies, denies, or abandoned stores. Also walk carefully in or around these as pressure-release devices are easily concealed under relatively small objects.

k. Areas in which boobytraps are not found immediately. Never assume without further investigation that entire areas are clear.

l. Obvious trip wires. The presence of one trip wire attached to an object does not mean that there are no others. Searching must be complete.

68. Indoor Searching Techniques

Those in charge of disposal teams should:

a. Assign no more than one man to a room in a building.

b. Indicate the finding of a large charge by a prearranged signal. All teams except those responsible for neutralizing large charges must then vacate the building immediately by the original route of entry.

c. Examine both sides of a door before touching a knob. Observe through a window or break open a panel. If doors and windows must be opened and both sides cannot be examined, use a long rope.

d. Move carefully in all buildings, for boobytraps may be rigged to loose boards, moveable bricks, carpets, raised boards or stair treads, window locks, or door knobs.

e. Never move furniture, pictures, or similar objects before checking them carefully for release devices or pull wires.

f. Never open any box, cupboard door, or drawer without careful checking. Sticky doors, drawers, or lids should be pulled with a long rope.

g. Not sit on any chair, sofa, or bed before careful examination.

h. Never connect broken wires or operate switches before checking the entire circuit. Such action may connect power to a charge.

t. Remove all switch plates and trace all wires that appear foreign to a circuit. Examine all appliances.

j. Investigate all repaired areas. Look for arming holes. Enlarge all wall and floor punctures. Cavities may be examined by reflecting **a** flashlight beam off a hand mirror. (This is also applicable for searching under antitank mines.)

k. Empty all fire boxes, remove the ashes, check fire wood, and move the coal pile.

l. Always work from the basement upward. Check, move, and mark everything movable including valves, taps, levers, controls, screens, and the like. A clockwork delay may not be heard if it is well hidden.

m. Double check basements and first floors—especially chimney flues, elevator and ventilator shafts, and insulated dead-air spaces. Check straight flues and shafts by observing from one end against a light held at the other. Dog-leg flues may be checked by lowering a brick from a safe distance.

n. Guard all buildings until they are occupied.

o. When possible and only after a thorough check, turn on all utilities from *outside* the building.

Note. A soldier by training can develop his sense of danger. Also by experience and careful continuous observation of his surroundings while in a combat area, he can develop an acute instinct that warns him of danger—a most valuable asset toward self-protection.

Section II.   DISARMING METHODS

69.   Neutralization

a. This is the making of a dangerous boobytrap safe to handle. If this is not possible, however, it must be destroyed. Neutralization involves two steps—*disarming* or replacing safeties in the firing assembly and *defuzing* or separating the firing assembly from the main charge and the detonator from the firing assembly.

b. Although types of boobytraps found in conventional warfare in a combat zone vary greatly, equipment used by most armies is basically similar except in construction details. Accordingly, a knowledge of the mechanical details and techniques in the use of standard U.S. boobytrapping equipment in conventional warfare prepares a soldier to some extent for dealing with that of the enemy. This, however is not true in guerrilla warfare. Most enemy boobytraps found recently in guerrilla infested areas, were cunningly and ingeniously improvised and laid. Such boobytraps can rarely be neutralized even by the most experienced specialists. These are discussed and illustrated in chapter 5.

c. Boobytraps may be neutralized by two methods. (1) Whenever the location permits, they may be destroyed by actuating the mechanism from a safe distance or detonating a charge near the main charge. These should be used at all times unless tactical conditions are unfavorable (2) When necessary, boobytraps may be disassembled by hand. As this is extremely dangerous, it should be undertaken only by experienced and extremely skillful specialists.

Note. Complete knowledge of the design of the boobytrap should be obtained before any neutralization is attempted.

d. In forward movements, all complicated mechanisms found are bypassed. These are marked and reported for neutralization later, when more deliberate action may be taken without harrassment by enemy fire.

e. All boobytraps exposed to blast from artillery fire or aerial bombing should be destroyed in place.

f. Boobytraps with unrecognizable or complicated firing arrangements should be marked and left for specialists to disarm.

(1) Electrically fired boobytraps are among the most dangerous **of** all. Though rare in the past, they now turn up frequently in guerrilla warfare. Some may be identified by the presence of electric lead wires, dry cells, or other batteries. Some are small containers with all elements placed inside which actuate at the slightest disturbance. These can hardly be disarmed even by experts.

(2) Another difficult type has delay fuzing—a spring-wound **or** electric clockwork for long delay periods or chemical action firing devices. As the time of detonation is uncertain, such boobytraps should be destroyed in place, if possible or tactically fesasible.

70. Rules of Conduct

a. Keep in constant practice by inspecting and studying all known boobytrap methods and mechanisms.

b. Develop patience. A careless act may destroy you and others as well.

e. Remember that knowledge inspires confidence.

d. Let only one man deal with a boobytrap. Keep all others out **of** danger.

e. If in doubt, get help from an expert.

f. Never group together when there is danger.

g. Be suspicious of every unusual object.

h. Regardless of nationality, consider every enemy a ruthless, cunning and ingenious killer.

71. Detailed Operations

a. Destruction in Place.

(1) If damage is acceptable, which is generally the case out **of** doors, the operator may initiate boobytrap riggings by their own mechanism or by a rope from a safe position (at least 50 meters away).

(2) The easiest method of getting rid of a boobytrap is to detonate a pound of high explosive adjacent to the main charge.

b. Removal of Main Charge (Antitank Mine).

Careful probing or search around the charge is necessary **to** locate and neutralize all antilift devices. Recognition of **the type of** firing mechanisms used is necessary to avoid casualty. **All safety** devices must be replaced. If complete neutralization seems doubtful, the charge should be pulled from place by a grapnel or rope from a safe location. After the charge is pulled, the operator should wait at least 30 seconds as a safeguard against a concealed delay action fuze.

c. Hand Disarming. None but trained specialists should undertake this job, unless the boobytrap's characteristics and disarming techniques' are well known. Trained specialists only should inspect and destroy all unusual or complicated mechanisms for safety reasons and for information on new enemy devices. The following procedures for hand neutralization are for guidance only, as the exact sequence depends on the type of device and the manner of placement.

(1) Do not touch any part of a boobytrap before examining it thoroughly. Locate all firing devices and their triggering mechanisms.

(2) When tracing wires, look for concealed intermediate devices laid to impede searching. Do not disturb any wires during the examination of the boobytrap.

(3) Cut loose trip wires only after careful examination of all connecting objects and their functions and replacing all safeties.

(4) Trace taut wires and disarm all connected firing devices by replacing safeties. Taut wires should be cut only when the danger at both ends has been eliminated.

(5)) Replace safeties in all mechanisms, using nails, lengths of of wire, cotter pins, and other objects.

(6) Never use force in disarming firing devices.

(7) Without disturbing the main charge, cut detonating cord or other leads between the disarmed firing devices and the main charge.

(8) Cut wires leading to an electric detonator—*one at a time.*

(9) When using a probe, push it gently into the ground. *Stop* when you touch any object. It may be a pressure cap or plate.

(10) Once separated, boobytrap components should be removed to a safe storage or disposal area.

d. Special Precautions.

(1) Be very cautious in handling delay mechanisms. Although there may be little danger before the appointed time, auxiliary firing devices may be present. All complicated and confusing devices should be destroyed in place or marked for treatment by specialists.

(2) Explosive containers of wood or cardboard, buried for long periods are dangerous to disturb. They are also extremely dangerous to probe if in an advanced state of decomposition. Deteriorated high explosives are very susceptible to detonation. Thus destruction in place of a boobytrap and in a concentrated area long exposed to moisture may detonate many others simultaneously.

(3) Metallic explosive containers, after prolonged burial, are often dangerous to remove. Oxidation may make them resistant to detection. After a time the explosive may become contaminated, increasing the danger in handling. Explosives containing picric acid are particularly dangerous as deterioration from contact with metal forms extremely sensitive salts readily detonated by handling.

(4) Fuzes of certain types become extremely sensitive to disturbance from exposure to wet soil. The only safe method of neutralizing or removing such deteriorated boobytraps is detonation in place.

72. Explosive Disposal

a. Usually, explosive items recovered by hand neutralization are destroyed by specially-trained explosive ordnance disposal units. Should untrained troops be required to do this, they should follow established procedures with great care. Explosives to be detonated should be buried in a pit at least 4 feet deep under 2 feet of earth, free of rocks or other matter that may become flying debris.

b. Components should be placed on their side or in position to expose their largest area to the force of the initiating explosive. Demolition blocks should be used for destruction of these components, if available; but bangalore torpedoes or dynamite may be substituted. Primed charges should always be connected to firing mechanisms by detonating cord, so that blasting caps may be connected at the last minute. This eliminates opening the pit in the event of a misfire. All persons engaged in disposal should take cover when explosive components are detonated. Despite the 2-foot layer of earth, fragments may be thrown at high velocity for several hundred yards.

INDEX

FM 4-30.16
MCRP 3-17.2C
NTTP 3-02.5
AFTTP(I) 3-2.32

FM 4-30.16   US Army Training and Doctrine Command
                                               Fort Monroe, VA

MCRP 3-17.2C   US Marine Corps Combat Development Command
                                                  Quantico, VA

NTTP 3-02.5   US Navy Warfare Development Command
                                                  Newport, RI

AFTTP(I) 3-2.32   US Air Force Doctrine Center
                                                 Maxwell AFB, AL

15 February 2001

EXPLOSIVE ORDNANCE DISPOSAL
Multiservice Procedures for EOD in a Joint Environment

TABLE OF CONTENTS

FIGURES

TABLES

PREFACE

1. Scope

This multiservice tactics, techniques, and procedures (MTTP) manual provides guidance and procedures for the employment of an explosive ordnance disposal (EOD) force when operating in a joint capacity throughout the range of military operations.

2. Purpose

This manual identifies standard tactics, techniques, and procedures (TTP) among the services for planning, integrating, and executing EOD operations in a joint environment. It sets forth TTP to assist joint activities and performance of the entire EOD force and establishes the procedures necessary to protect all United States (US) military and coalition personnel and operations.

3. Application

This publication applies to all leaders, planners, and the EOD warfighter when deploying forces into any theater. The TTP established in this manual apply to the commanders of combatant commands, subunified commands, joint task forces (JTFs), and subordinate components of these commands.

4. Implementation Plan

Participating service command offices of primary responsibility will review this publication, validate the information, and reference and incorporate it in service and command manuals, regulations, and curricula as follows:

Army. The Army will incorporate the TTP in this publication in US Army training and doctrinal publications as directed by the Commander, US Army Training and Doctrine Command (TRADOC). Distribution is in accordance with Department of the Army (DA) Form 12-99-R.

Marine Corps. The Marine Corps will incorporate the TTP in this publication in US Marine Corps (USMC) training and doctrinal publications as directed by the Commanding General, US Marine Corps Combat Development Command (MCCDC). Distribution is in accordance with the Marine Corps Publication Distribution System.

Navy. The Navy will incorporate the TTP in US Navy doctrine and training publications as directed by the Commander, US Navy Warfare Development Command (NWDC). Distribution is in accordance with MILSTRIP Desk Guide and Navy Supplemental Publication 409.

Air Force (AF). AF units will validate and incorporate appropriate procedures in accordance with applicable governing directives as validated by Headquarters (HQ), AF Civil Engineer (CE). Distribution is in accordance with Air Force Instruction 33-360 as directed by the Air Force Doctrine Center (AFDC).

5. User Information

a.   The TRADOC-MCCDC-NWDC-AFDC Air Land Sea Application (ALSA) Center is the proponent for this publication with the joint participation of the approving service commands. ALSA will review and update this publication as required.

b.   We encourage recommended changes for improving this publication. Key comments to specific chapters and subjects while providing a rationale for each recommendation. Send comments to—

Army

Commander
US Army Training and Doctrine Command
ATTN: ATDO-A
Fort Monroe, VA 23651-5000
DSN 680-3454 COMM (757) 727-3454
E-mail: doctrine@monroe.army.mil

Marine Corps

Commanding General
US Marine Corps Combat Development Command
ATTN: C42
3300 Russell Road – Suite 318A
Quantico, VA 22134-5021
DSN 278-6233 or 34 COMM (703) 784-6233/4

Navy

Commander, Navy Warfare Development Command
ATTN: ALSA Liaison Officer
1530 Gilbert Street
Norfolk, VA 23511-2723
DSN 262-2782   COMM (757) 322-2782

Air Force

Headquarters Air Force Doctrine Center
ATTN: DJ
216 Sweeney Boulevard, Suite 109
Langley Air Force Base (AFB), VA 23665-2722
DSN 574-8091 COMM (757) 764-8091
E-mail: afdocdet1@langley.af.mil

ALSA

ALSA Center
ATTN: Director
114 Andrews Street
Langley AFB, VA 23665-2785
DSN 575-0902 COMM (757) 225-0902
E-mail: alsa.director@langley.af.mil

EXECUTIVE SUMMARY

EOD

Multiservice Procedures for
Explosive Ordnance Disposal in a Joint Environment

This manual—

- describes service-specific EOD organizations, capabilities, equipment, doctrine, and training.
- provides joint EOD command and control (C^2) considerations.
- provides guidance for planning and conducting EOD operations in a joint environment.
- establishes procedures for information management (IM), and operational and intelligence reporting.

Introduction

This publication documents the C^2 considerations and procedures for conducting EOD operations in a joint environment. These TTP are necessary to coordinate and integrate multiservice EOD operations to facilitate efficient and safe joint EOD operations. The EOD force performed in a joint capacity during many recent operations; however, most of the command relationships and coordination requirements were *ad hoc*. Each service routinely deploys EOD forces into a theater, and assigns the force based on service needs rather than the theater needs as a whole. This MTTP provides many considerations for employing EOD forces in a joint capacity and provides C^2 options for the geographic combatant commander and commander, joint task force (CJTF) to consider. This MTTP also highlights the EOD capabilities and force structures for each service.

Concept and Organization

Chapters I and II highlight the significant joint C^2 issues when preparing to employ EOD forces. The focus of the service chapters (Chapters III-VI) is for the benefit of non-EOD commanders and staff and EOD commanders and staff from other services to gain an understanding of the personnel/equipment and doctrine utilized within the other services. Finally, in an effort to expedite C^2 requirements for the senior theater EOD commander, the MTTP offers standardized EOD reporting formats which each service has agreed to use when operating in a joint environment. Countering unexploded explosive ordnance (UXO) and the threat it creates during all operations is challenging. This MTTP provides the necessary command structure to assist (rather than impair) efficient EOD operations. This challenge becomes easier as the level of knowledge regarding other services' EOD forces and their contributions to the mission increase.

Command and Control

By capturing methods used to coordinate joint EOD operations, this publication offers three command relationship options in how to best employ the entire EOD force:

- Service-component responsibility (with direct liaison authorized [DIRLAUTH]).
- Lead-service component (with or without tactical control [TACON] or operational control [OPCON] of other service EOD forces).
- Subordinate Joint EOD Task Force (JEODTF).

Other C^2 considerations when utilizing these task organization options include:

a. The geographic combatant commander or CJTF can modify or mix these options to the theater mission, threat, and situation.

b. The MTTP establishes methods for creating a joint EOD operations center (JEODOC) to assist and streamline the management of EOD operations at a single command, normally under the direction of the J-4.

c. The JEODOC is useful whenever joint EOD management requirements are beyond the capability of the J-4 and/or the subordinate EOD force headquarters. Both the Army and Navy have existing C^2 EOD units around which a JEODOC or JEODTF headquarters can be built. Specifically, the Army's battalion (O-5 command) and group (O-6 command) headquarters, or the Navy's Mobile Unit (O-5 command) and group (O-6 command), provide a ready EOD headquarters unit to quickly manage or command joint EOD operations.

Chapters

Chapter I – Introduces the Department of Defense (DOD) EOD mission, capabilities, and common characteristics of the EOD force. The chapter also provides a historical perspective of EOD operations and the impact the threat has had on US operations.

Chapter II – Describes the purpose for conducting EOD operations as a joint force and provides three distinct employment options for the CJTF to consider when employing EOD forces. This chapter also provides guidance for standing up a JEODOC or a JEODTF.

Chapter III – Provides the reader an understanding of Army EOD operations to include the Army EOD mission, service doctrine, Army organizations and capabilities, and specific Army EOD training.

Chapter IV - Provides the reader an understanding of Marine Corps EOD operations to include the USMC EOD mission, service doctrine, Marine Corps organizations and capabilities, and specific EOD training opportunities.

Chapter V – Discusses the Navy EOD mission and naval EOD doctrine. The chapter also focuses on Navy EOD operations to include Navy EOD organizations and capabilities and specific Navy EOD training opportunities.

Chapter VI – Presents AF EOD operations to include AF EOD mission, service doctrine, and specific AF EOD training.

Appendices

Appendix A – Offers a multiservice capabilities matrix for commanders and planners to understand what capabilities each service can and can not provide.

Appendix B - Provides a CJTF staff or EOD staff officer with a logical checklist of necessary EOD planning requirements during each stage of an operation.

Appendix C – Describes the procedures for standing up a JEODTF, and the responsibilities of each service's EOD force. Also identifies EOD-specific JEODTF staff requirements and provides an example of a notional JEODTF staff.

Appendix D – Formulates and describes the required EOD reports, and standardizes reporting requirements when operating in a joint environment.

Appendix E – Captures the recurring EOD operations each service routinely conducts.

PROGRAM PARTICIPANTS

The following commands and agencies participated in the development of this publication:

Joint

DOD EOD Technology and Training Secretariat, Indian Head, MD
Joint Warfighting Center, Fort Monroe, VA
Joint Staff, J34, Combating Terrorism, Washington, DC
Commandant, Naval School EOD, Eglin AFB, FL

Army

HQ, DA, ATTN: DALO-AMA-EOD, Washington, DC
HQ, TRADOC, Deputy Chief of Staff, Doctrine (ATTN: ATDO-A), Fort Monroe, VA
US Army Pacific, ATTN: EODCT, Fort Shafter, HI
TRADOC Munitions System Manager, Redstone Arsenal, AL
HQ, 52d Ordnance Group (EOD), Fort Gillem, GA
HQ, 79th Ordnance Battalion (EOD), Fort Sam Houston, TX
HQ, 184th Ordnance Battalion (EOD), Fort Gillem, GA
US Army Technical Detachment, NAVEODTECHDIV, Indian Head, MD
Army EOD Training Representative, Fort Lee, VA
Army Engineer School, Fort Leonard Wood, MO

Marine Corps

Marine Corps Combat Development Command, Joint Doctrine Branch (C427) and Ground Branch (C422), Quantico, VA
Marine Corps Base, EOD, Quantico, VA
HQ, USMC Logistics, Planning and Operations, Washington, DC
2d Marine Air Wing, Cherry Point, NC
Seventh Engineer Support Battalion, Camp Pendleton, CA
Eighth Engineer Support Battalion, Camp Lejeune, NC

Navy

NWDC, ALSA Liaison Officer (LNO), Norfolk Naval Base, Norfolk, VA
Commander, EOD Group ONE, San Diego, CA
Commander, EOD Group TWO, Norfolk, VA

Air Force

HQ, USAF CE, Washington, DC
Air Force Doctrine Center, Detachment 1, Langley AFB, VA
Air Combat Command, CE/EOD Division, Langley AFB, VA

Air Force CE Support Agency, Tyndall AFB, FL
Air Force Special Operations Command, CE/EOD Division, Hurlburt Field, FL
Air Force Materiel Command, CE/EOD Division, Wright-Patterson AFB, OH
HQ, AF Space Command, CE/EOD Division, Peterson AFB, CO
HQ, Air Mobility Command, CE/EOD Division, Scott AFB, MO
Air Education Training Command, CE/EOD Division, Randolph AFB, TX
HQ, USAF Europe, Ramstein AFB, CE/EOD Division, Germany
HQ, Pacific Air Force, CE/EOD Division, Hickam AFB, HI
75th CE Group, Hill AFB, UT
56th CE Squadron, Luke AFB, AZ
USAF EOD Liaison Officer, Central Command, Tampa, FL
Detachment 63, Aircraft and Armament Center, Indian Head, MD

Chapter I

EOD WITHIN THE
DEPARTMENT OF DEFENSE

1. Mission

The mission of DOD EOD is to support national security strategy and force protection by neutralizing hazards from foreign and domestic, conventional, nuclear, biological or chemical (NBC) UXO, and improvised explosive devices (IEDs) that present a threat to operations, installations, personnel, or materiel.

2. Threat

The increasing potential of UXO resulting from the proliferation of arms, ammunition, and explosives throughout the world, and an increasing number of terrorist attacks threaten the mobility and survivability of the entire force. Area denial-type munitions containing antidisturbance, influence, self-destruct, remote control, booby-trap, or contact fuzing also directly threaten US forces. The increasing availability of NBC material, components, and weapons raises the possibility of terrorists using these weapons, or conventional IEDs, in an attack against civilian populations or military facilities and units. Wherever US forces deploy, these threats exist.

3. Capabilities

Military EOD personnel and equipment provide a variety of capabilities to commanders. Joint regulations and DOD directives prescribe specific responsibilities for each service. Common EOD training, equipment, and technical manuals provide each service with the capability to detect, identify, field evaluate, render safe, recover, and make final disposition of conventional or NBC UXO and IEDs, both foreign and domestic. Due to specific training and safety measures, equipment capabilities, and security issues, only EOD-qualified personnel can provide EOD support to US military operations. See Appendix A, Multiservice EOD Capabilities Matrix, and individual service chapters (chapters III-VI) for a detailed listing of specific service EOD capabilities.

4. Common Characteristics

a.   History. The development of the US military EOD force was an outgrowth of the bitter experience of the British at the beginning of World War (WW) II, when the Germans dropped thousands of bombs and mines containing large explosive charges on land and in the waters around Great Britain. The US started an EOD service shortly before entering WWII by sending representatives from each of the military branches to England for bomb disposal training. Those representatives returned to the US and established separate Army and Navy bomb disposal schools. By 1960, DOD combined the Army and Navy schools under Navy cognizance to become the Naval EOD School. In 1971, DOD designated the Secretary of the Navy as the single manager for EOD technology and training.

b. Multiservice EOD School. The Naval School EOD (NAVSCOLEOD) located at Eglin AFB, FL, is a Navy command, staffed by Army, Navy, AF, and Marine Corps instructors. The EOD course of instruction is approximately six months in length for Army, AF, and Marine Corps personnel and twelve months long for Navy personnel. Navy personnel receive additional instruction in diving procedures and underwater ordnance operations. NAVSCOLEOD trains officer and enlisted personnel from all services in munitions identification, render-safe procedures, explosives safety, and EOD-unique equipment. The school's mission is to provide EOD-trained individuals to the operating forces of all US services and to provide training to various federal agencies and international students.

c. EOD Research and Development. The Navy is assigned as the single manager for all DOD EOD research and development, training and evaluation, and common-type training. The Naval EOD Technology Division (NAVEODTECHDIV), Indian Head, MD, is a Navy command with colocated detachments of all services, which is responsible for research and development of specialized EOD tools, equipment, techniques, and procedures common to two or more services. This research and development assists EOD units in maintaining a modern capability to detect/locate, render safe, or dispose of UXO and associated hazards. All services can submit requirements to the NAVEODTECHDIV for equipment development and can provide input to the prioritization and selection of projects for development. The services also provide final approval and acceptance of developed items.

d. EOD Technical Manuals. All services use the same EOD technical manuals as the basis for EOD training and technical procedures. The NAVEODTECHDIV develops and publishes these technical manuals and receives joint service input and approval prior to publication. The NAVEODTECHDIV limits access to EOD publications to EOD-qualified personnel who are performing EOD duties. The NAVEODTECHDIV regularly exchanges information with both US national agencies and allied ordnance experts to stay abreast of the latest UXO trends and threats.

e. Common Equipment. All military EOD teams possess the same basic EOD tools to detect, identify, evaluate, render safe, and perform final disposition of explosive devices and associated hazards. These tools include portable x-ray equipment, robots, specialized demolition charges, and specialized tools for removing fuzes. Each service has specialized EOD equipment to perform service-unique EOD missions.

5. Interoperability

The existing multiservice training and technical manuals, common equipment, and jointly supported research and development program make EOD one of the most interoperable specialties in the US military. Multiservice EOD forces have worked side by side in numerous operations during recent contingencies and conflicts. These joint EOD operations demonstrate the potential for greater planning and operational efficiency in the future.

Chapter II

EOD IN A
JOINT ENVIRONMENT

1. Operations

a.   Background. UXO and other hazardous devices in a theater of operations will likely threaten military forces and operations. US personnel have been killed or injured by UXO in virtually every conflict or contingency in which the US has participated. The UXO threat is more serious to noncombatants, who are unfamiliar with military ordnance. While service components usually deploy with, and are supported by, its own EOD assets, the number of these assets is very limited and in high demand. In many situations, the geographic combatant commander, through his directive authority for logistics, can achieve economy of effort by organizing his EOD forces using common servicing. Common servicing may allow the joint force commander (JFC) to provide more efficient and effective EOD support to the joint force depending on the operational scenario. The joint EOD force could also include integration of coalition EOD forces in a joint/coalition EOD task force (TF).

b.   Historical Examples. During recent US contingencies, EOD assets from different services combined their efforts to maximize the efficiency of EOD operations. While effective, most were accomplished in an *ad hoc* manner, often improvised on site between the local EOD commanders.

(1)   Desert Storm. During the major UXO cleanup effort in Kuwait immediately after Desert Storm, EOD forces from each of the services were organized into a *de facto* subordinate EOD JTF under Task Force Freedom. The JTF dealt with the large numbers of UXO remaining in Kuwait City. This organizational technique allowed the task force and subordinate EOD commanders to focus all available EOD assets on the major UXO clean-up effort in an organized and efficient manner, thus reducing the need for individual services to bring more EOD assets into the country.

(2)   Somalia. In Somalia, EOD forces from the Army, AF, and Marines operated together to remove UXO by sharing response sectors in Mogadishu. Navy EOD personnel supplemented Army EOD soldiers in destroying captured munitions at an improvised demolition range.

(3)   Bosnia. In support of continued peacekeeping efforts in Bosnia, US EOD forces were integrated to provide EOD services for the elimination of UXO and to support conventional/special operations and coalition forces.

c.   Planning. A common servicing approach for EOD support is often the most efficient means to address the UXO threat, especially when a limited number of EOD forces are available. Factors affecting the structure of a joint EOD force include intelligence and terrorist threats, parent unit mission (for example: flight operations, demining, or support to Special Operations Forces [SOF]). Appendix B, EOD Planning Checklist for Joint Operations, provides general EOD planning guidance to support contingency operations.

2. Employment Options

a.   Background. The magnitude of the UXO threat in the joint operations area (JOA), coupled with the overall operational situation, normally determines the value added and degree of common servicing desired for EOD support.

b.   JFC Options. This chapter provides three options for structuring a joint EOD force to accomplish the theater mission. Each option and organizational examples depict the use of service forces to accomplish the EOD mission. If the geographic combatant commander uses a functional command structure for the theater, the JFC logistics directorate of a joint staff (J-4) would still have overall responsibility, with service forces performing the EOD mission. Based on the situation, the CJTF can modify or mix any of the following options:

(1)   Service-component responsibility (with DIRLAUTH).

(2)   Lead-service component (with or without TACON or OPCON) of other service EOD forces.

(3)   Subordinate JEODTF.

3. Service Component Responsibility with DIRLAUTH

a.   Utilization. The service-component responsibility employment option is used when each service component provides for and controls its own EOD forces and requirements. It is also the most common method of employing EOD forces, although this option often will not provide the most efficient or responsive use of EOD assets.

b.   Benefits. This option works best when—

(1)   the service component geographical areas of responsibility within the JOA are clear.

(2)   the operational situation allows deployment of each of the service component's EOD forces.

(3)   the JFC does not require direct control of EOD missions.

c.   DIRLAUTH Option. Commanders may benefit by specifying DIRLAUTH between the service component's EOD units. Previous EOD operations have routinely operated in this manner; however, DIRLAUTH often was not expressly written in the operation plan (OPLAN) or operation order (OPORD). Formalizing DIRLAUTH often provides a more efficient and responsive method for coordinating EOD operations among the service components. See Figure II-1, Service-Component Responsibility (with DIRLAUTH) Organization.

d. Employment Considerations. This employment option—

(1) allows each service to retain control of its EOD assets for operations in its area of responsibility (AOR).

(2) does not always allow the most efficient or responsive use of EOD assets.

(3) will likely increase response time to a major accident or incident when support is required to cross service-component lines.

(4) increases intelligence and operational information sharing between the service components when DIRLAUTH is authorized.

(5) may benefit the JFC and staff by establishing a JEODOC to assist in managing the EOD mission. Paragraph 6 of this chapter provides the conditions for establishing a JEODOC and its functions.

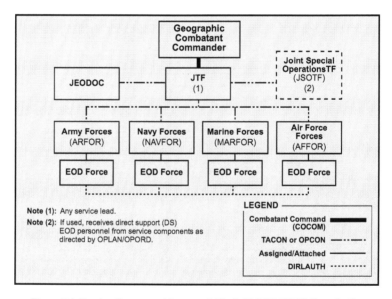

Figure II-1. Service-Component Responsibility (with DIRLAUTH) Organization

4. Lead-Service Component (with or without TACON or OPCON) Option

a.   Utilization. The combatant commander may use the lead-service component option to support a limited duration mission or to provide more efficient EOD support, especially in a short notice, austere environment mission (for example: Bosnia and Kosovo). In this option, the combatant commander, through his directive authority for logistics, assigns specific EOD-related missions to a specific service component with or without TACON/OPCON of other services' EOD forces.

b.   Formation. To establish a lead-service component, the combatant commander, in consultation with his subordinate JFC and service-component commanders, assigns specific common EOD tasks to a lead-service component. Normally, the lead-service component for EOD functions within a JFC is the service component with the majority of EOD requirements in theater. Another consideration for appointing a lead service is to appoint the component most capable of conducting the EOD mission. The combatant commander may place selected EOD assets from one or more of the other service components TACON or OPCON to the lead-service component EOD commander to assist in accomplishing the assigned tasks. Other services providing forces to the lead service may provide, or be directed to provide, staff augmentation to the lead-service EOD commander's staff. These services should, as a minimum, provide LNOs. Having other service EOD staff augmentation or LNOs within the lead-service EOD staff section expedites planning, coordination, and mission execution. This option must include a support relationship for administrative/logistics support. Figure II-2, Lead-Service (with or without TACON/OPCON) Organization, depicts a typical lead-service command relationship.

c.   Employment Considerations. This option—

(1)   allows more efficient use of limited EOD assets for JTF-specific missions of limited duration or high priority. This option is not used to provide EOD support for specific service-related missions (to include aircraft support, harbor clearances, and carrier battle-group support). Each service retains select EOD forces to accomplish service-specific missions.

(2)   centralizes all routine EOD operation taskings and data tracking with a single point of contact (POC), normally the lead-service component EOD unit operations officer.

(3)   improves technical intelligence acquisition and dissemination to all EOD forces.

(4)   may benefit the JFC and staff by establishing a JEODOC to assist in managing the EOD mission. The conditions for establishing a JEODOC and its functions are discussed in paragraph 6 of this chapter.

(5)   provides a mechanism that plans for fluctuations of service EOD force responsibilities as the operation transitions through different phases. Allows service EOD support to increase or decrease based on operational tempo or the theater EOD mission.

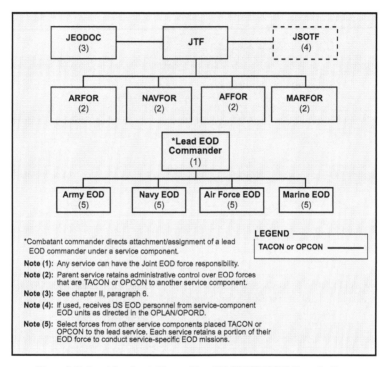

Figure II-2. Lead-Service (with or without TACON/OPCON) Organization

5. Subordinate JEODTF

a. Utilization. A JEODTF is a subordinate JTF that controls (via TACON/OPCON for attached units) two or more service-component EOD organizations and is jointly staffed. Task organizing EOD forces under a JEODTF allows the CJTF to focus limited EOD assets where they are needed most and provides an opportunity to optimize EOD mission capabilities. It also serves a similar function as a JEODOC, but includes command authority, as opposed to staff management, over assigned and attached EOD forces.

b. Formation. The CJTF should base the decision to establish a JEODTF on specific mission needs, while also considering ongoing service component EOD requirements. Based on JFC guidance and other considerations, such as an OPLAN and existing agreements, each service component provides assets to fulfill common EOD support requirements within the JOA. However, even when common EOD support is provided for by a lead service or JEODTF, service-unique EOD requirements remain the responsibility of the individual service components. The combatant and subordinate JFCs should consider the common support reqirements needed to allow service-components the ability to execute their service-specific requirements. See Figure II-3, JEODTF Organization. The JEODTF headquarters normally is built around an existing service-component EOD command, with augmentation from other service EOD staff personnel. When using a JEODTF, the CJTF must ensure that adequate administrative, logistical, and medical support is available to the JEODTF. The CJTF employs a JEODTF for a limited time for a specific mission to clear hazards that threaten theaterwide operations. See Appendix C for more details on establishing a JEODTF.

    c.   Employment Considerations. The JEODTF option—

        (1)   delegates the authority to organize forces to accomplish the EOD mission, based on the CJTF's concept of the operation. By design and to avoid duplication of effort, a JEODOC is not established if the JEODTF option is used.

        (2)   provides the EOD force with unity of effort, centralized planning, and decentralized execution.

        (3)   consolidates the capabilities of each service's EOD force in a joint effort to solve theaterwide UXO hazards.

        (4)   facilitates the combatant commander/CJTF control over EOD forces and missions.

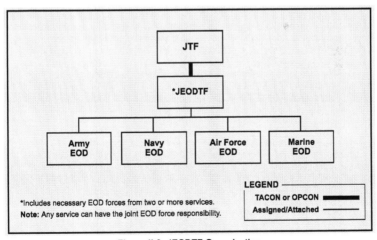

Figure II-3. JEODTF Organization

(5) expedites technical intelligence/data acquisition and dissemination to end-users.

(6) provides a command structure for the integration and control of coalition EOD forces.

(7) may be most appropriate for a major theater war (MTW), munitions storage or transportation disasters, large operations, or post-hostilities UXO clean-up operations.

6. JEODOC

a. Formation. The JFC and J-4 staff determine the need for the JEODOC. The JEODOC is useful whenever joint EOD management requirements are beyond the capability of the JTF's J-4 staff or subordinate EOD force headquarters. The scope of the assigned mission and allocated force structure determines the staffing level and overall support requirements. The JEODOC is a fully integrated and mobile facility, manned and equipped by the individual service components under the auspices of the JTF J-4. To avoid duplication of effort, a JEODOC is not established when a JEODTF is formed. Both the Army and Navy have existing C^2 EOD units around which a JEODOC is built. Specifically, using the Army's battalion (O-5 command) and group (O-6 command) headquarters, or the Navy's Mobile Unit (O-5 command) and group (O-6 command), provide a ready EOD headquarters unit to quickly establish a JEODOC.

b. Functions. The JEODOC is a multifunctional operational center under the auspices of the JTF J-4. Its primary purpose is to manage theater-level UXO hazard-reduction operations and EOD planning, integrating, coordinating, and tasking functions (through the direction and authority of the commander) when there is no subordinate JEODTF formed to accomplish this task. The JEODOC provides the JTF oversight over all EOD operations in theater, tracks critical EOD assets, monitors and recommends changes in priorities, and resolves issues between service components. The JEODOC tasking authority enables the JTF to change service-component EOD force responsibilities as the operation transitions through different phases. This allows service EOD support to increase or decrease based upon operational tempo or the theater EOD mission. The major functions resident in the JEODOC are—

(1) Operations/Intelligence (Ops/Intel) Section. The ops/intel section ensures current theater-EOD operations are synchronized with CJTF intent. It monitors, synchronizes, and reports EOD operations to ensure maximum efficiency throughout the JOA. The section also monitors and interprets the enemy and friendly situation for the commander and informs forces of significant changes in operations, objectives, and priorities.

(2) Administrative/Logistics (Admin/Log) Section. The admin/log section identifies immediate or potential problems in the support or material system. The section determines logistics support resource requirements,

coordinates airlift requests, and special transportation requirements, and provides feedback (on request) for mission-essential repair and support items.

(3)   Communications-Electronics (C-E) Section. This section provides information systems planning, coordination, and support to the JEODOC and all joint, coalition, and external organizations, as required.

7. Information Management and Reporting

a.   Information Management (IM). IM refers to the processes a JTF J-4, JEODOC, and JEODTF use to obtain, manipulate, direct, and control vital EOD-related information. IM for EOD operations includes all processes involved in the creation, collection and control, dissemination, storage and retrieval, protection, and destruction of critical EOD information. The goal of IM for EOD operations is to provide a timely flow of quality information, enabling the commander of any EOD force to anticipate and understand the consequences of changing conditions. See FM 3-99.4 (FM 101-4)/MCRP 6-23A/ NWP 3-13.1.16/AFTTP(I) 3-2.22, *Multiservice Procedures for Joint Task Force–Information Management.*

b.   Reporting Requirements. See Appendix D, Standardized EOD Reports.

Chapter III

ARMY EOD OPERATIONS

1. Interservice Responsibilities

Army Regulation (AR) 75-14; Chief of Naval Operations Instruction (OPNAVINST) 8027.1G; Marine Corps Order (MCO) 8027.1D; and Air Force Joint Instruction (AFJI) 32-3002, *Interservice Responsibilities for Explosive Ordnance Disposal*; and AR 75-15, *Responsibilities and Procedures for Explosive Ordnance Disposal*, define the Army's responsibilities as the following:

   a.   To provide support to Army installations/activities and to render safe/ dispose of explosive ordnance in the physical possession of the Army.

   b.   To establish, operate, and support an explosive ordnance reconnaissance program.

   c.   To provide routine and emergency response to all land-mass areas under US control, except those specifically assigned as a responsibility of the Navy, Marine Corps, or Air Force.

2. Mission

The Army EOD mission is to support national security strategy by providing the capability to neutralize hazards from conventional UXO, NBC and associated materials, and IED (both explosive and NBC), that present a threat to operations, installations, personnel, and/or material. Army EOD forces also may dispose of hazardous foreign or US ammunition, UXO, individual mines, booby-trapped mines, and chemical mines. Routine clearing and rapid breaching of foreign or US minefields is the responsibility of the Army engineers. EOD provides the Army with a rapidly deployable support package for the elimination of hazards from UXO in any operational environment. The EOD force serves as a combat multiplier by neutralizing UXO that is restricting freedom of movement and denying access to supplies, facilities, and other critical assets. Army EOD forces equip, train, and organize to support tactical land forces across the spectrum of operations, to include peacekeeping, military operations other than war (MOOTW), and MTW.

3. Doctrine

   a.   Rules of Allocation. The Army has sufficient EOD force structure to support two simultaneous MTWs in separate theaters of operations. The Army allocates each theater one EOD group at Army/theater level; three EOD battalions at theater support command/corps/division level; and 28 EOD companies at specified locations that best support the maneuver commander. See Figure III-1, US Army EOD Theater Force Structure.

   b. C^2. The EOD group provides C^2 for all Army EOD assets and operations in theater. The EOD battalions provide C^2, mission tasking, technical intelligence acquisition and management, and limited administrative and logistic support for up to 10 EOD companies. EOD battalions, or battalions (-), may deploy as the senior C^2 element for Army EOD operations in a given operation. Ordnance companies remain under the command of their parent battalion, but depending on the operational situation, may be placed TACON/OPCON to another unit. When utilizing the TACON/OPCON C^2 option, the parent battalion retains administrative control (ADCON) of their subordinate companies. EOD companies provide general support (GS) on an area basis or direct support (DS) to specified elements in support of operations. The combatant commander's planning staff tailors EOD forces to support specified operations down to a brigade combat team. Responsibilities of the EOD commander at all levels include—

   (1)   recommending policy and distribution of EOD assets.

   (2)   monitoring EOD support missions and establishing workload priorities.

   (3)   serving as POC for technical intelligence coordination.

   (4)   coordinating GS and DS EOD support.

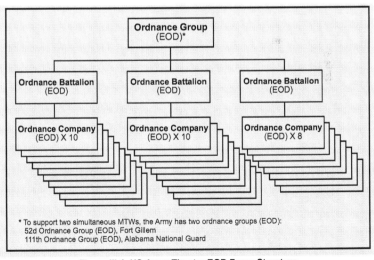

Figure III-1. US Army Theater EOD Force Structure

(5) ensuring each EOD unit establishes provisions for communications at each level to support EOD operations.

(6) supplementing other theater force-protection procedures to meet the existing threat.

(7) coordinating administrative and logistical support, as required, from the supported command.

c. Operational Planning. The EOD group and EOD battalion provide staff planning for Army EOD operations throughout their area of operations (AO). Thus, the EOD group commander is also the EOD special staff officer to the Army force commander, joint force land component commander (JFLCC), and coalition JFLCC. The EOD battalion commander serves as the EOD special staff officer at the corps JTF and coalition JTF level. In the absence of a deployed EOD group or EOD battalion, the senior-ranking Army EOD officer also serves as the EOD staff officer for the Army element. The EOD commander is responsible for providing the EOD annex to all OPLANs/ OPORDs. This ensures that EOD forces fully understand and support the maneuver commander's operations and also provides for force protection throughout the AO.

d. Theater-Level Strategic Planning. The Army service component commander (ASCC) and his staff plan for Army and assigned EOD theater-strategic EOD requirements in support of the geographic combatant commander's campaign plan. The ASCC accomplishes the planning by using the Joint Operation Planning and Execution System (JOPES) and coordinates the planning effort with the combatant commander's EOD staff officer. The EOD battalion and group commander may provide LNOs to the geographic combatant commander or JFC staff if required. The EOD battalion commander may also provide an LNO to a brigade, division, or corps JTF headquarters if deemed necessary by operational requirements. The LNO ensures—

(1) mutual cooperation and understanding between commanders and staffs of different headquarters.

(2) coordination on tactical matters to achieve mutual purpose, support, and action.

(3) precise understanding of stated or implied coordination measures to achieve synchronized results.

e. Combined Operations. Combined operations involve the military forces of two or more nations acting together in common purpose. The EOD battalion/group commander considers military doctrine and training, equipment, cultural differences, and language barriers when providing TACON or OPCON of alliance or coalition EOD forces. Lessons learned indicate that few linguists have both the technical expertise and depth of understanding to cross both language and doctrinal boundaries and be fully understood when dealing with UXO and technical EOD procedures. Combined operations require a significant resource commitment to dedicated liaison and linguist teams from alliance or coalition EOD forces.

4. Organizations

The Army assigns EOD organizational assets to specified major command (MAJCOM) areas. See Figure III-2, US Army EOD Force Allocation. The

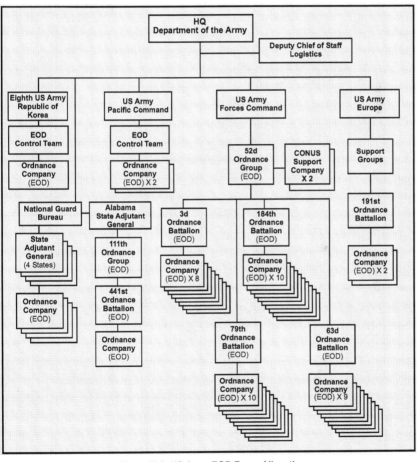

Figure III-2. US Army EOD Force Allocation

Army numbers all EOD units for support to specified OPLANs. Major EOD commands and their locations are:

a. US Army Forces Command: 52d Ordnance Group (EOD), four EOD battalions, and 39 EOD companies.

b. US Army Europe: EOD cell, 191st Ordnance Battalion, and two EOD companies.

c. US Army, Pacific Command: EOD control team and two EOD companies.

d. Eighth US Army, Republic of Korea: EOD control team and one EOD company.

e. US Army National Guard: one EOD ordnance group, one EOD battalion, and five EOD companies.

5. Capabilities

a. The EOD Company–Mission. Each EOD company is authorized 23 soldiers, comprising 20 EOD-qualified technicians, including the commander and first sergeant, and three support soldiers (personnel clerk, mechanic, and supply sergeant). The EOD companies provide GS to the corps on an area basis and can perform DS missions for a specific maneuver unit, normally a division or brigade TF. Due to the limited support personnel, the EOD company depends on the supported unit for administrative and logistical support.

b. The EOD Company–Force Capabilities. The activity of EOD intensifies based upon the operational tempo of the battle and stabilizes as the theater matures. The EOD force within a theater of operations can expect to conduct operations in a myriad of situations and locations. An EOD company can field up to seven EOD teams, consisting of a minimum of one EOD team leader and one EOD team member. Each team can operate for a period up to 72 hours and may conduct 8-10 EOD incidents in a 24-hour period. This is dependent on the mission, enemy, terrain and weather, troops and support available, time available (METT-T). The Army adds a "C" at the end of METT-T for civilian considerations. Manpower intensive EOD operations (multiple UXO, NBC operations, and ammunition supply point accidents) require several EOD teams at one time to complete the mission. EOD commanders can task organize their teams as necessary to complete the mission.

c. Operational Capabilities. Organic to each EOD company are personnel and equipment to identify, mitigate, neutralize, remove, and dispose of conventional or NBC explosive hazards. These hazards may arise from domestic or foreign ordnance or IED that degrades the commander's mobility or that threaten personnel, operations, or installations. Many of the capabilities are non-service specific. To avoid repetition in the service chapters, Appendix E provides those capabilities that are recurring, non-service specific EOD requirements. Key Army-specific EOD operational capabilities are—

(1)   Force Protection. Army EOD provides the bomb disposal component of the Army's force protection program. In addition to actual response to explosive devices, Army EOD forces can also provide training in UXO/explosives recognition and reporting, bomb threat search procedures and evacuation, site vulnerability assessments, and unit standard operating procedures (SOP) preparation and validation. This training increases the effectiveness of the maneuver commander's force protection program.

(2)   Very Important Person Protective Support Activity (VIPPSA). Army EOD is the executive agent for coordination and tasking of all military EOD support for the US Department of State (DOS) and US Secret Service (USSS) for the protection of the president, vice president, and designated foreign heads of state.

(3)   Amnesty Programs. Army EOD units assist in the collection and disposal of hazardous munitions and components as part of the maneuver commander's force protection program, to ensure the continued safety of military personnel.

(4)   Stuck Rounds. Each EOD team performs specialized procedures to remove artillery or mortar rounds that become stuck in firing tubes.

(5)   Mortuary Services. Immediate recovery and clearance of deceased persons is a priority of the services. The presence of UXO being found on or imbedded in deceased persons adversely impacts the recovery of coalition or US personnel. Therefore, Army planners normally involve EOD-qualified leaders in planning and conducting recovery and processing of deceased personnel.

d.   Continental US (CONUS) Support Company. The Army assigns two CONUS support companies to the EOD group. The CONUS support company assumes responsibility for the CONUS Army EOD mission upon deployment of an EOD battalion and all, or some, of its subordinate EOD companies. The CONUS support company commander provides C^2 of an operations section and disperses a response force or teams at up to six different geographical locations. The CONUS support company can assume many of the C^2 functions of the deployed battalion, to include—

(1)   coordination of EOD support to the USSS.

(2)   EOD support to military installation commanders.

(3)   EOD support to other civilian agencies.

The group can also task the companies to provide specialized support to the National Command Authority (NCA) for response to counterterrorism activities and response to weapons of mass destruction (WMD).

6. Training

a. Required Individual EOD Training. All Army EOD specialists attend the Army-specific material/equipment training (Phase II) at Redstone Arsenal, AL. Army EOD personnel also receive continuous technical sustainment training and evaluations at their units of assignment.

b. Specialized Training Opportunities. Select EOD soldiers may also attend specialized training such as technical escort specialist, advanced access and disablement, advanced EOD, and a variety of nuclear and chemical operations courses. A limited number of specially selected EOD soldiers also attend Federal Bureau of Investigation civilian EOD training or foreign EOD courses, such as the British Army Engineer IED Disposal and Advanced Manual Techniques Course, the Canadian Military Forces IED Disposal Course, and the French Military Demining School.

c. Combat Training Centers. EOD companies and company elements provide support to maneuver forces (battalions, brigades, and division TF headquarters) undergoing training at the Joint Readiness Training Center, National Training Center, and the Combat Maneuver Training Center. Specifically, countering UXO hazards with EOD teams prevent needless deaths, injuries, and destruction of the commander's combat power. During reception, staging, onward movement, and integration, supporting EOD teams provide UXO danger awareness and risk management, fratricide prevention, and other safety instruction to JTF personnel.

Chapter IV

MARINE CORPS EOD OPERATIONS

1. Interservice Responsibilities

MCO 8027.1D; AR 75-14; OPNAVINST 8027.1G; and AFJI 32-3002, *Interservice Responsibilities for Explosive Ordnance Disposal*, states that the USMC EOD forces provide EOD services on USMC installations, in assigned operational areas, or for explosive ordnance in the physical possession of the Marine Corps.

2. Mission

The USMC EOD mission is to provide force protection in support of the Marine air-ground task force (MAGTF). This is accomplished by neutralizing hazards from foreign, domestic, conventional, and NBC UXO and IEDs that present a threat to operations, installations, personnel, or material. Additionally, Marine Corps EOD units provide technical intelligence on ordnance through disassembly and rendering munitions inert.

3. Doctrine

a. Operational Concept. Marine EOD forces conduct operations to enhance survivability/mobility, preserve warfighting capabilities, and to enable Marine expeditionary and joint forces to achieve and maintain battlespace dominance through the reduction or elimination of UXO threats.

b. C^2. The EOD officer/team leader directs and coordinates the execution of EOD tasks in support of the commander's intent. The EOD teams within Marine expeditionary forces (MEFs) and subordinate MAGTFs must coordinate with each other to ensure complete support of all units. The senior EOD officer has staff responsibility for all EOD-related matters during a contingency or conflict.

c. Operational Planning. For planning, EOD falls under the Pacific/ Atlantic/MEF Marine Corps component logistics staff officer (Marine Corps brigade or higher staff) (G-4). The senior EOD Marine for a future mission conducts all operational planning. Due to the inherent danger of UXO, commanders should include the EOD officer/team leader in all phases of planning. This Marine is responsible for providing the EOD annex for OPLANs/OPORDs to ensure full EOD support in all phases of the operation.

4. Organizations

a. Marine EOD Forces. Marine EOD forces within the MEFs consist of an EOD platoon within the engineer support battalion (ESB) of the force service support group contained within the division and EOD forces within the Marine wing support squadron (MWSS) of the Marine wing support group.

(1) The EOD Platoon of the ESB. The ESB EOD platoon is a part of the headquarters and services (H&S) company of the ESB. The ESB S-3 tasks and controls the EOD platoon. See Figure IV-1, which depicts the H&S company of the ESB. Organization and equipment for the EOD platoon provides eight fully capable teams for operations in support of the MEF. See Figure IV-2, USMC EOD Platoon, Engineer Support Battalion, for a depiction of the eight teams. These eight teams can reorganize into smaller teams and respond to separate incidents, depending upon the complexity of the UXO/IED incident. A six-man EOD team will support a Marine expeditionary unit (special operations capable) (MEU[SOC]). The MEU (SOC) is the most

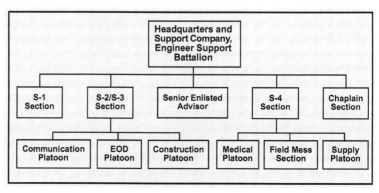

Figure IV-1. USMC H&S Company, Engineer Support Battalion

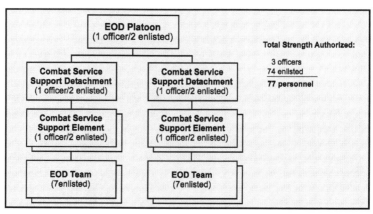

Figure IV-2. USMC EOD Platoon, Engineer Support Battalion

commonly deployed version of a MAGTF. The Marine Corps assigns the EOD team to the MEU service support group (MSSG) operations officer. During MEU operations, the EOD team may be OPCON/TACON to a higher headquarters to facilitate the most efficient use of a scarce asset.

(2) EOD Section of the MWSS. The EOD section of the MWSS consists of one officer and six enlisted personnel and primarily supports the air combat element. The MWSS EOD section is capable of providing full EOD support to an expeditionary airfield (EAF). Each team may reorganize into smaller teams and respond to separate incidents. For example, the EOD team may operate at a forward operating base, EAF, forward arming and refueling point, or may respond to a separate UXO incident. See Figure IV-3, USMC EOD Section, Marine Wing Support Squadron.

b. Marine Base/Air Station EOD Forces.

(1) Marine Corps Bases. The base EOD teams are under OPCON of the Assistant Chief of Staff, Operations and Training, department of the Marine Corps base. The EOD team usually consists of one officer and six enlisted and provides full EOD support for all operational and training evolutions that the base conducts.

(2) Marine Corps Air Stations (MCAS). The Marine Corps assigns this EOD team as a special staff section to the air station commanding officer. This section usually consists of one officer and four enlisted personnel and provides all support in the conduct of operations and training aboard the MCAS.

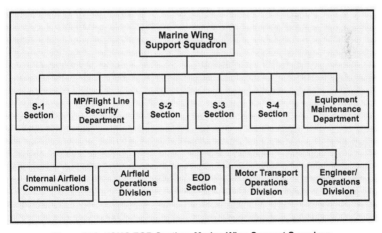

Figure IV-3. USMC EOD Section, Marine Wing Support Squadron

5. Capabilities

a. Marine EOD Team Capabilities. In addition to the recurring operations provided in Appendix E, all Marine EOD teams have the following capabilities—

(1) Tactical Recovery of Aircraft or Personnel (TRAP). The EOD technicians assist in extracting personnel from aircraft and the recovery, rendering safe, or destruction of any remaining explosive and classified components as required. Marine EOD technicians that support/participate in a TRAP operation are under OPCON of the search team leader.

(2) Base Recovery After Attack. EOD provides rapid UXO clearance after an attack to facilitate rapid reopening of an airfield for combat operations. A UXO hazard can disrupt and/or paralyze air operations and do so for long periods of time. These disruptions/interruptions to operations are particularly applicable to targets requiring rapid reopening priority. Regardless of the munitions employed against an airbase, base recovery, and, in particular, airfield recovery must take place in the shortest time possible. Multiple factors effect when and how the rendering safe and clearance of UXO occurs during a recovery mission. These factors include, but are not limited to—

(a) sensitivity of the fuzing.

(b) condition of the munition.

(c) location of the munition.

(d) priority of clearance assigned to the location.

(3) Noncombatant Evacuation Operation (NEO). The EOD team neutralizes any explosive hazards capable of endangering the NEO party/ security forces or evacuating personnel. These explosive hazards can include conventional or improvised UXO. The EOD team can also destroy any contraband, weapons, or explosives brought into the site. During an NEO, the site commander normally has TACON of the EOD team for optimal utilization.

(4) Humanitarian Assistance (HA) Operations. Marine EOD units conducting an HA operation provide mobile training teams. These teams destroy weapons, ordnance, and explosives, and report ordnance-related information to the proper authority. The EOD units support MAGTF internal security by responding to IEDs and by providing instruction to MAGTF units concerning ordnance identification and IED awareness. The optimal method of employing an EOD unit during an HA is by TACON to the operations officer.

(5) Force Protection. The optimal method of employing EOD forces during force protection operations is by providing DS to the MAGTF. Employment of the EOD force requires application of planned and integrated security programs, including—

(a) combating terrorism.

(b) physical security.

(c) operations security.

(d) personal protective security supported by intelligence.

(e) counterintelligence

(f) other security programs.

The EOD force within the MAGTF normally receives direction from the force protection officer of the MAGTF. Attachment of EOD teams to subordinate units should only occur when the supported unit is separated from the MAGTF and response by individual tasking is not feasible.

(6) Technical Support and Training. EOD units provide technical intelligence through exploitation of ordnance by identification, disassembly, and rendering munitions inert. Additionally, Marine EOD personnel teach awareness, response, reporting, and identification of IEDs and locally manufactured ordnance items. EOD units perform crater analysis and assist in post-blast investigations. The MAGTF can attach EOD forces to raid units to neutralize munitions/missiles.

(7) Dynamic Entry. Dynamic entry involves the use of specialized technical entry methods against a specific target. EOD performs the dynamic entry mission in support of the maritime special purpose force (MSPF) and military police (MP) special response teams. Methods include the use of mechanical tools, thermal torches, shotguns, and explosives. Dynamic entry methods ensure 100 percent penetration of the target using a minimum of force, with the intent to limit collateral damage. These operations support in-extremis hostage rescue and raids to destroy or rescue equipment/ personnel in support of the MSPF or MP special response teams.

(8) Disaster Areas. If a disaster strikes an area where munitions are manufactured, stored, or utilized, EOD support may allow relief forces to conduct operations and to safeguard citizens.

b. Marine Corps MOOTW EOD Capabilities. During MOOTW and smaller scale contingencies, EOD forces recover, render safe, and dispose/ neutralize ammunition/UXO, and clear IEDs used by guerrilla or paramilitary units.

c. MEU (SOC) EOD Capabilities. MEU (SOC) EOD units provide EOD-related capabilities in the following operations:

(1) Maritime Intercept Operation (MIO). The purpose of an MIO is to board and search shipping vessels that may be handling contraband or are potentially hostile to national interests. The USMC often attaches EOD teams to a unit conducting a visit, board, search, and seize (VBSS) operation. The EOD teams search for and render safe or destroy IEDs and other hazardous devices.

(2) Gas and Oil Platform (GOPLAT) Operation. A GOPLAT is an operation when the NCA dictates use of oil and gas production platforms as a staging/listening/operating base, or the US deems it necessary to capture the platform. The Marine Corps assigns an EOD team to the assault force of a

GOPLAT to neutralize IEDs and to perform special demolition procedures to destroy critical locations (if necessary).

(3) In-Extremous Hostage Rescue (IHR). The Marine Corps conducts this mission to protect American and foreign lives that have been held hostage or prisoner when a point of death situation arises. The Marine Corps assigns EOD technicians to the maritime special purpose force during deployment. The assault unit EOD technicians must qualify on assault skills to operate as part of the team during all phases of the operation. During the IHR, the EOD technicians clear explosive devices and are members of the dynamic entry teams. The EOD technicians assist the person or persons tasked with breaching (establishing an entry point) to facilitate surprise and speed of entry.

6. Training

a.   Team Qualification Requirements. All EOD technicians are graduates of basic EOD school and possess some or all of the skills listed in paragraph b below, through MEU training rotation and follow-on training at their unit.

b.   MEU-Specific Courses. The following courses are MEU-specific training opportunities:

(1)   Specialized demolitions.

(2)   Dynamic entry and close-quarters battle courses.

(3)   Training in the urban environment.

(4)   Special operations exercises (taught by the Special Operations Training Group from the 1st, 2d and 3d MEF).

Marines also attend Basic Airborne School, Fort Benning, GA; the Combat Divers School, Panama, FL; and the Small Boat Training Landing Force Training Center within the Pacific and Atlantic Fleets.

Chapter V

NAVY EOD OPERATIONS

1. Interservice Responsibilities

OPNAVINST 8027.1G/AR 75-14/MCO 8027.1D/AFJI 32-3002, *Interservice Responsibilities for Explosive Ordnance Disposal*, defines the Navy EOD mission. US Navy (USN) EOD provides services on naval installations; within oceans and contiguous waters, up to the high water mark of harbors, rivers and coastal environments; and emergency response to land mass not specifically assigned as a responsibility of the Army, Marine Corps, or AF.

2. Mission

The USN EOD mission is to support national security strategy by providing forces capable of conducting land and underwater detection, identification, render safe, recovery, field evaluation, and disposal of explosive ordnance.

3. Doctrine

The Navy generally categorizes EOD operations into three types: maritime operations, contingency operations, and ordnance intelligence and acquisition.

a. Maritime Operations. The Navy conducts EOD operations to enhance ship survivability, preserve fleet warfighting capabilities, and enable naval, expeditionary, and joint forces to achieve and maintain battlespace dominance through the reduction or elimination of hazardous UXO threats. The Navy assigns EOD forces to aircraft carrier battlegroups (CVBG), amphibious ready groups (ARG) and mine-countermeasures groups, special contingency operations at sea and ashore, and shore installations where continuing EOD requirements exist. Operational commanders employ these forces as necessary to meet theater objectives.

b. Contingency Operations. EOD forces support contingency operations in support of US forces and operations in the interest of national security and safety. Their flexibility and interoperability facilitate partnership with Special Warfare and Marine Corps forces when threats involve conventional ordnance or WMD. From their dedicated fleet and shore assignments, EOD forces support federal and local authorities in the rendering safe and disposal of explosives and explosive devices and assist the USSS in presidential and very important person (VIP) protection. EOD forces also support the Coast Guard in counternarcotics operations and participate in MOOTW such as maritime interdiction, NEO, disaster relief, and security assistance surge operations.

c. Ordnance Intelligence and Acquisition. Navy EOD personnel are qualified divers and can recover ordnance items on land or underwater, make the ordnance explosively safe, and return the item for exploitation. EOD detachments gather immediate preliminary intelligence on threat ordnance in the field. This intelligence is then disseminated to those requiring it in the AO until the detachment or other asset can conduct a more detailed exploitation. Data collected contributes to the development of render-safe procedures and supports the development of countermeasures, as well as determining the location of enemy stockpiles, types of launch platforms, and tactics.

4. Organizations

The Navy organizes EOD forces to support the geographic combatant commanders. The geographic combatant commander has OPCON of EOD forces through the fleet commanders and numbered fleet commanders. Staff officers within each of these organizations provide C^2 and staff planning support for operational EOD activities. See Figure V-1 for a depiction of the Atlantic Fleet and European EOD organizational structure and Figure V-2 for the EOD organizational structure of the Pacific Fleet.

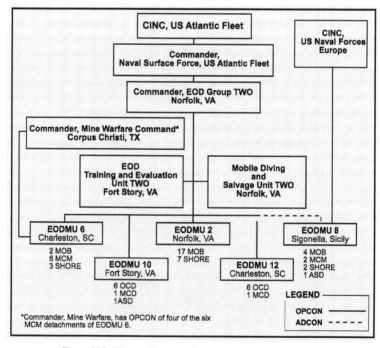

Figure V-1. Atlantic Fleet and European EOD Organization

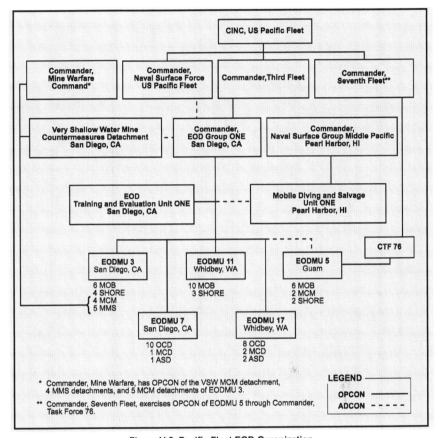

Figure V-2. Pacific Fleet EOD Organization

5. Capabilities

The fundamental operational entity within EOD is the detachment. A detachment is a subordinate entity, capable of independent operations, with assignment to EOD mobile units (EODMUs). The best method to describe Navy EOD capabilities is by listing the EOD detachment types. Appendix A identifies specific mission capabilities of each of the major Navy EOD detachments.

a. EOD Mobile (MOB) Detachments. These detachments provide EOD support to CVBGs, ARGs, and theater commanders. The Navy tasks MOB detachments with a variety of contingency operations to include range clearance, USSS support, organic mine countermeasures (MCM), humanitarian demining operations (HDO), riverine, port security/harbor defense operations, and to augment SOF. The EOD MOB detachment can perform in one of three main configurations—a CVBG deployment, an ARG deployment, and contingency deployments.

(1) EOD MOB Detachments–CVBG Deployments.

(a) Mission. The MOB detachment's mission is to provide an EOD warfare capability to the deployed CVBG commander. Navy EOD provides response during flight deck operations involving live, fuzed ordnance, and ordnance replenishment evolutions. Also, Navy EOD provides a rapid response to ordnance incidents within the CVBG and a forward deployable capability for response to contingencies outside of the CVBG. MOB detachments also provide support to maritime interdiction forces, NEO, and other contingency operations in a MOOTW environment and participate in bilateral multinational exercises. MOB detachments can perform a limited amount of minor ships underwater repair tasks. Mobility capabilities include fastrope, rappel, helicopter cast and recovery, specialized personnel insertion/ extraction (SPIE) and helicopter deployment of combat rubber raiding craft (CRRC). EOD personnel from these detachments may split into smaller response elements. Normal manning is one officer and seven enlisted personnel.

(b) Assignment. The Navy assigns an EOD MOB detachment to each deploying CVBG as a task element. To coordinate C^2 of the MOB detachment within the CVBG, assignment of the detachment is to the CVBG commander. A separate EOD officer and senior enlisted EOD technician is colocated on the CVBG commander's platform with the EOD officer performing duties as the task element commander. The EOD officer that performs the task element commander functions also acts as the EOD LNO to plan and direct the employment of detachments/elements as appropriate.

(2) EOD MOB Detachment-ARG Deployment.

(a) Mission. The mission and capabilities are similar to those provided to a CVBG with the additional emphasis of supporting amphibious operations afloat and ashore.

(b) Assignment. The Navy assigns an EOD MOB detachment to each ARG/MEU. The ARG/MEU further assigns the detachments to the deployed amphibious squadron/amphibious group. To best coordinate C^2 of the MOB detachments within the ARG, the ARG commander has OPCON of the detachment. The ARG commander assigns the detachments as task elements under the amphibious task group. The host ship(s) have TACON of the detachments. Normal manning is one officer and seven enlisted personnel.

(3) EOD MOB Detachments–Contingency Operations Deployment. When the Navy tasks an EOD MOB detachment to perform in a MOOTW environment, the detachment provides EOD personnel to support primary

forces engaged in contingency operations including insurgency/ counterinsurgency, counterterrorism/antiterrorism, peacekeeping, maritime interdiction, NEO, disaster relief, counterdrug, and security assistance surge operations. Normal manning is one officer and seven enlisted. The EOD MOB detachment performs the following operations in support of contingency operations:

(a) Special Operations Support. EOD forces frequently operate in support of SOF. In Vietnam, Grenada, Panama, and the Persian Gulf, EOD provided direct mission support to dispose of antipersonnel devices, IEDs, and UXO that impeded operations. Any MOB detachment can perform contingency operations in a MOOTW environment such as VBSS or insurgency/counterinsurgency action in support of special operations. Additionally, the Navy permanently assigns a limited number of EOD personnel to the Navy Special Warfare Development Group.

(b) Counternarcotics. The increase in the use of IEDs in the narcotics trade has significantly expanded EOD-force participation in counternarcotics operations. EOD personnel conduct diving and search operations in support of the US Coast Guard, US Treasury, and US Customs Service in counternarcotics and drug interdiction.

(c) EOD Support to Non-DOD and Civilian Organizations. The executive manager for EOD technology and training provides EOD research, technology, and training support to the USSS, the Federal Bureau of Investigation, the Central Intelligence Agency, the US Coast Guard, and the Federal Aviation Administration. The executive manager provides assistance to other organizations designated by the Secretary of Defense. The Navy provides EOD assistance to render safe and dispose of IEDs, nonmilitary commercial explosives, and similar dangerous articles upon request from federal agencies or civil authorities.

b. Fleet Antiterrorist Security Team. The commander, EOD Group TWO assigns a detachment from EODMU TWO to support these operations. This detachment augments a Marine company on a rotational basis, as required. Their mission is to support geographical areas experiencing heightened tension resulting from a terrorist threat or regional instability. Normal manning is one officer and seven enlisted personnel.

c. Shore-Based (SHORE) Detachments. The Navy locates EOD SHORE detachments at shore activities that require continuous EOD support. Their mission is to provide an EOD capability to the activity to which they are assigned. EOD support includes general ordnance handling, transportation, storage, disposal and/or safety missions, live-fire training, range clearance, and underwater ordnance testing. The operational commander may deploy the assigned detachment for area or regional response in support of military and civilian incidents or accidents requiring EOD warfare skills. The specific mission determines the actual manning requirements of a SHORE detachment.

d. MCM Detachments.

(1) Mission. EOD MCM detachments are part of the dedicated mine warfare force and are specialized detachments that locate, identify, neutralize, recover, exploit, and dispose of sea mines. These detachments provide the MCM commander with an underwater capability. They normally conduct integrated operations with surface MCM (SMCM) and airborne MCM (AMCM) units and are also capable of limited independent operations. MCM detachments maintain basic warfighting capabilities equivalent to those of MOB detachments in the conventional ordnance and IED threat response areas. MCM detachments have special low-influence signature (magnetic and acoustic) equipment and capabilities. The detachments are also responsible for recovering new mine types and subsequently conducting tactical field exploitation of the recovered mines, a mission critical to the effectiveness of all MCM operations. Normal manning is one officer and seven enlisted personnel.

(2) Assignment. The Navy often assigns MCM detachments under OPCON of an MCM squadron commander. Each deploying MCM squadron normally consists of a command/support ship, an AMCM unit, an SMCM unit, and an underwater MCM (UMCM) unit. The UMCM command task unit is normally the commanding officer of EODMU THREE or EODMU SIX (or their designated representative). The UMCM task unit normally consists of two or more MCM detachments and other EOD detachments as assigned. The EOD command task unit is the MCM squadron commander's primary advisor for planning and executing safe and efficient UMCM operations.

e. Marine Mammal System (MMS) Detachments. MMS detachments provide an enhanced capability to detect, identify, mark, render safe, recover, and neutralize objects within the water column as well as those that have become buried under the ocean's floor. All MMS detachments are mobile systems that can rapidly deploy to most areas of the world on short notice utilizing fixed-wing aircraft, helicopters, trucks, boats, amphibious ship well decks, or command ship. The Navy's current marine mammal program has one fleet operational site and one fleet support facility, both located in San Diego, CA. These highly mobile, reliable, and effective systems provide a trained, contingency response capability in the following mission areas:

(1) Mark (MK) 4 Module (MOD) 0 MMS (Close-Tethered, Deep-Moored Minehunting, and Neutralization System). This MMS detachment is an underwater surveillance and detection system which employs dolphins for object location, marking, and recovery with the mission of detecting and neutralizing close-tethered, deep-moored mines. The system provides an effective tool for port break-in and breakout missions as well as MCM operations at naval choke points, anchorages, along known/suspected mine routes (Q-routes) and in vital sea lanes. Normal manning is one officer and 18 enlisted personnel.

(2) MK 5 MOD 1 MMS (Pingered Object Recovery System). This MMS detachment is a recovery system that uses sea lions to locate and attach

recovery hardware to mines and test ordnance with acoustic pingers attached to them. Normal manning is one officer and 13 enlisted.

(3)   MK 6 MOD 1 MMS (Swimmer Detection and Defense System). This MMS detachment is a waterside security system that uses dolphins to protect harbors, anchorages, and individual assets against unauthorized swimmers, divers, and swimmer delivery vehicles. It can be employed in MOOTW, antiterrorist, or traditional port and anchorage scenarios. Normal manning is one officer and 20 enlisted personnel.

(4)   MK 7 MOD 1 MMS (Bottom and Buried Minehunting and Neutralization System). This MMS detachment is a mine detection, location, and neutralization system that uses dolphins to detect and neutralize proud mines (mines on the ocean floor) and mines buried under the ocean bottom. Normal manning is one officer and 25 enlisted personnel.

f.   Area Search Detachments (ASDs).

(1)   ASD Underwater Systems. ASDs detect and locate underwater ordnance on the ocean bottom by using side-scan sonar, towing hardware/ cables, and precise navigation systems. The sonar and associated equipment are portable and have a relatively small logistic footprint for employment on an ASD craft of opportunity. Although ASDs are flexible and mobile, their effectiveness is largely limited to areas of smooth and hard bottoms. Buried mines, certain mine shapes, cluttered and uneven bottoms, and moored mines reduce the effectiveness of ASDs for MCM operations. Normal manning is one officer and four enlisted personnel.

(2)   ASD Deployment and Mission. ASDs deploy from EODMUs or mobile diving and salvage units (MDSU) to perform underwater search operations to locate salvageable objects such as aircraft or large debris to be removed from sea lanes. These operations occur during channel conditioning operations and support the conduct of port breakouts and overseas port facility recovery operations. ASDs also use their assets to reacquire mine-like objects previously detected by other MCM assets and systems. EOD ASDs provide a limited mine-detection capability when a low-profile presence or very rapid response is desired, and the increased risk to the host platform is acceptable. ASDs can pass position data and mark contacts for prosecution by EOD MCM detachments and can operate in both salt and fresh water.

g.   Fly-Away Recompression Chamber Detachment. This detachment provides emergency hyperbaric recompression treatment for personnel who experience diving-related injuries when a local chamber is not available. The fly-away recompression chamber can locate on an MCM command/support ship, a craft of opportunity, or ashore. Normal manning is three divers, one diving medical technician, and one diving medical officer.

h.   Very Shallow Water (VSW) MCM Detachments.

(1)   VSW Mission. The mission of the VSW MCM detachment is to provide a small cadre of specially trained and equipped forces to conduct

low-visibility mine exploration and reconnaissance operations in the VSW zone (10-40 feet). Primary functional areas include: confirming the presence or absence of mines in selected VSW areas, re-acquiring and identifying previously detected mine-like contacts in the VSW zone, and providing the tactical commander with data from VSW zone exploratory and reconnaissance missions to predict mine density. Supporting functional areas involves diving and demolition operations. VSW MCM forces must apply primary and supporting functional areas described above by employing specific VSW MCM-unique equipment, procedures, and tactics to counter the VSW mine threat.

(2)   VSW Assignment and Operations. VSW serves as a component of the Navy's dedicated MCM forces under OPCON of commander, mine warfare command, and ADCON of commander, EOD Group ONE. The detachment participates in fleet MCM exercises and conducts regular fleet training to develop and refine VSW MCM tactics. Additionally, they serve as a warfighting laboratory for assessing the performance of new technologies to address MCM reconnaissance in the VSW zone. In the event of contingency operations, the VSW detachment maintains a 48-hour fly-away capability for short-notice embarkation in advance force platforms assigned under the commander, amphibious task force (CATF) and the MCM commander when the MCM commander is assigned under the CATF. The VSW detachment can mobilize with specialized equipment and tactics to enhance advance force and pre-assault MCM capabilities in support of amphibious operations in a mined environment. Current manning totals 70 personnel—seven officers and 46 enlisted personnel from the Navy and one officer and 16 enlisted from the Marine Corps.

i.   EOD Command, Control, Communications, Computers, and Intelligence (C^4I) Cell. Individual EOD and MDSU detachments are currently assigned in support of various OPLANs/contingency plans (CONPLANs). As multiple detachments deploy, EOD forces may deploy as a single unit under the control of their commanding officer. Operations may require employment of EOD detachments simultaneously in close proximity or rapidly dispersed to remote areas for independent operations. Accordingly, an EOD C^4I capability is required to assist in eliminating fratricide and providing force identification and logistical support. Experience during Desert Storm, numerous exercises, and MOOTW have routinely demonstrated that an EOD C^4I cell provides effective C^4I, logistics, and medical support to the deployed EOD and MDSU detachments. The deployed EOD C^4I cell also facilitates organic support capabilities to sustain operations for long periods. Normal manning is two officers and seven enlisted personnel.

j.   Naval Reserve Force (NRF) EOD Detachments. NRF EOD detachments are maintained within the NRF EODMUs. They provide contributory support during peacetime and crisis response during MOOTW, major regional conflicts, and contingency operations. NRF detachments are comprised of selected reserve personnel, who maintain capabilities in diving, basic demolition, ordnance location, identification, and disposal. There are three types of NRF EOD detachments: ordnance clearance detachments (OCDs), mobile communications detachments (MCDs), and ASDs.

(1)   OCDs. OCDs provide diving and demolition support, perform manpower-intensive EOD-related tasks that enable EOD detachments to be available for more technical procedures, and act as force multipliers when integrated with regular forces. OCDs can locate, identify, and destroy conventional ordnance, but they do not perform render-safe or exploitation procedures. OCDs train and qualify on basic use of the low-signature diving equipment (MK 16 underwater breathing apparatus [UBA]). OCDs conduct routine hull/pier/underwater searches, locate/identify/destroy underwater ordnance in support of MCM port clearance operations, and provide contributory support in the areas of search-and-rescue retrograde ordnance/ explosives disposal and range clearance operations. For MCM operations, OCDs work in conjunction with other MCM assets to provide additional identification and neutralization capabilities. Normal manning is one officer and six enlisted personnel.

(2)   MCDs. MCDs provide a deployable field communications cell for integrated command post tactical and strategic communications in support of EOD forces in the field. Capabilities include Global Command and Control System, secure voice, data, and imagery radio-frequency communications in the high frequency, ultrahigh frequency line of sight, satellite communications, and very high frequency spectrum. Normal manning is one officer and four enlisted personnel.

(3)   ASDs. ASDs were described in paragraph 5f above.

k.   MDSUs. In addition to assigned EOD units, EOD Group ONE and EOD Group TWO have ADCON over MDSU ONE and MDSU TWO, respectively. MDSUs provide mission-capable active and naval reserve detachments to perform diving, salvage/recovery, and underwater ship-repair operations in ports or harbors. They can operate from ports, US Navy and Military Sealift Command vessels, or commercial contract salvage or repair vessels. In addition, the MDSU detachments provide limited self-defense. Each MDSU has mobile diving and salvage detachments and fleet maintenance diving detachments. These detachments can simultaneously deploy to different areas of the world in support of their assigned mission areas.

6. Training

a.   Diver Training. EOD diver training, conducted at the Naval Diving and Salvage Training Center, Panama City, FL, qualifies Navy EOD technicians to perform self-contained underwater breathing apparatus (SCUBA), MK-16 mixed gas, and surface-supplied diving operations.

b.   Tactical Insertion/Extraction. EOD MOB and MCM detachments perform the tactical insertion and extraction of personnel and equipment by unconventional methods (for example SPIE, rappel, fastrope, casting, and

CRRC) in areas that cannot be accessed/reached by conventional means. Select mobile and shore detachments maintain land and water parachute-insertion capability for worldwide emergent support.

    c.   EOD Training and Evaluation Units (EODTEUs). EODTEUs provide readiness improvement training to EOD detachment personnel preparing for operational deployments. Detachments are guided through advanced TTP classroom training, followed by advanced practical exercises in all core mission areas. EODTEUs provide similar training to shore and naval reserve detachment personnel. Additionally, training units provide specialized, high-risk supervisory training for demolition/burn range operations, SPIE/rappel/fastrope operations, SCUBA/MK-16 UBA operations and field communications procedures. EODTEUs also conduct field evaluation of new and experimental EOD tools and equipment prior to distribution to operational units.

Chapter VI

AIR FORCE EOD OPERATIONS

1. Interservice Responsibilities

AFJI 32-3002; AR 75-14; OPNAVINST 8027.1G; and MCO 8027.1D, *Interservice Responsibilities for Explosive Ordnance Disposal*, define the AF EOD responsibilities. The AF EOD furnishes services on AF installations, dispersal bases (which include non-DOD installations from which air reserve component forces operate), in assigned operational areas, or for the disposal of explosive ordnance in the physical possession of the USAF. When requested by other services, federal agencies, or civil authorities, USAF EOD teams respond to any incident site to prevent or limit damage and injury.

2. Mission

The AF EOD mission is to protect people, facilities, and resources from damaging effects of UXO, hazardous components, and devices. The EOD personnel locate, identify, disarm, neutralize, recover, and dispose of hazardous explosives, NBC, and incendiary items. They also neutralize criminal and terrorist bombs when requested or directed by proper authority, clear areas of explosives-related contamination, and dispose of unserviceable and outdated munitions. The EOD force supports the USSS and the DOS in their protection of the president, vice president, foreign dignitaries, and VIPs. EOD forces train other USAF personnel on ordnance recognition, hazards, and precautions and provide EOD support to the global engagement mission.

3. Doctrine

a. Concept. The USAF organizes EOD force packages into unit-type codes (UTCs) to provide flexible structures to support contingency missions. The USAF designs these packages to meet specific manning and equipment requirements based on the mission and threat. Planners can combine the UTCs in building-block fashion to provide coverage for location-specific missions.

b. C^2. In peacetime, USAF assigns EOD units to a USAF wing under the base civil engineer (BCE) and further assigns the wings to the MAJCOMs through the numberedAir Forces. During deployed operations, USAF assigns EOD units under the deployed BCE (when one is assigned). If no BCE is assigned, EOD units normally work for the deployed wing/unit commander. At the wing level during increased threat conditions, the wing establishes a survival recovery center (SRC) for wing C^2. The senior EOD representative performs duties at the SRC to control all EOD operations at the deployed location.

c.   Operational Planning. The USAF provides basic UTC packages for planners to develop capabilities at deployed locations. These UTCs form capabilities to respond to the various threat levels. This building-block approach allows the maximum flexibility in EOD force employment. The USAF EOD UTCs are—

(1)   4F9X1-Civil Engineer Squadron (CES) Prime Base Engineer Emergency Force (BEEF) EOD Lead Team. This UTC consists of six personnel, EOD equipment, technical data, explosives, two vehicles (one M-1116 up-armored high-mobility multipurpose wheeled vehicle [UA-HMMWV] and one M1038 high-mobility multipurpose wheeled vehicle [HMMWV]), and one M101 trailer. The UTC supports MTW locations and contingency missions at aerial ports, en route bases, or critical CONUS operating locations. It also provides limited capability for MOOTW and force protection buildup. This UTC supports lead aviation squadrons by protecting critical resources and personnel from the effects of explosive hazards, minor munitions accidents, terrorist explosive devices, and UXO from limited enemy attack. Capabilities of the UTC include render safe US and foreign conventional and chemical hazards, and IEDs.

(2)   4F9X2-CES Prime BEEF EOD Follow Team. This UTC has four personnel with a limited set of EOD equipment, technical data, explosives, and one vehicle (M1038 HMMWV). The UTC augments an EOD lead team (4F9X1) to provide added support to both a lead and a follow aviation squadron.

(3)   4F9X3-CES Prime BEEF EOD Base Support/Sustainment Team. The base support/sustainment team has two personnel deploying with a set of base support equipment. This UTC includes robotic platforms for remote operations and augments the EOD lead team (4F9X1) and/or EOD follow team (4F9X2). This UTC can provide additional equipment for sustained operations.

(4)   4F9X6-CES Armored Base Recovery Vehicle. The 4F9X6 UTC consists of one M1116 UA-HMMWV that provides mobile, armored protection during ordnance reconnaissance and safing missions.

(5)   4F9X7-All-Purpose Remote Transport System (ARTS). The ARTS provides remote application of explosive tools for use against large IEDs and a remotely operated platform for removal of submunitions from operating areas. The ARTS also supports any deployed EOD capability for recovery from attack, force protection build-up, or accident clean-up operations.

(6)   4F9X9-CES Prime BEEF High Threat Augmentation Team. The high threat augmentation team consists of two EOD personnel with weapons, ammunition, and personal protective equipment. This UTC augments other UTCs in incremental levels by adding two additional personnel until necessary manpower requirements are met.

(7) 4F9XA-CES Prime BEEF EOD Leadership/Management Team. The 4F9XA UTC has one EOD officer and a chief master sergeant with personal weapons, ammunition, and personal protective equipment. This UTC supports forward-deployed staff positions and provides a C^2 capability for theater, JTF, or unit EOD teams.

(8) 4F9XB-CES Prime BEEF EOD Contingency Support Team. This UTC consists of six personnel, one vehicle, minimum EOD equipment, technical data, and explosives. This UTC supports en-route and force-protection missions.

4. Organizations

During peacetime, the AF assigns EOD flights to the CE organization within the MAJCOMs. They are responsible for peacetime support of the command mission and posturing deployable force packages. See Figure VI-1, Air Force Peacetime EOD Organization. In wartime, the EOD force deploys to support the geographic combatant commanders. See Figure VI-2, Air Force Wartime EOD Organization.

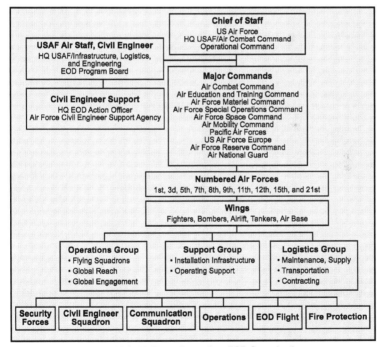

Figure VI-1. Air Force Peacetime EOD Organization

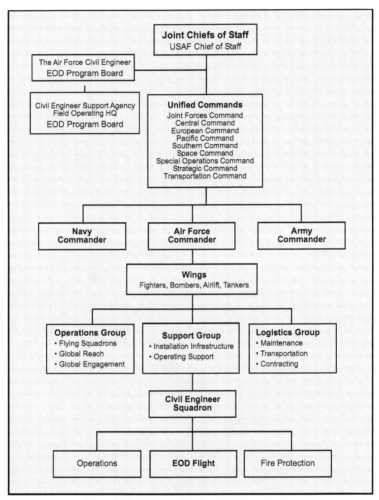

Figure VI-2. Air Force Wartime EOD Organization

5. Capabilities

a. General. The minimum EOD team size on incident responses is two qualified operators employing remote procedures whenever possible. If available, a third EOD-qualified supervisor provides on-scene safety, supervision, and command advice.

b.   Capabilities. In addition to the recurring, nonservice-specific EOD capabilities at Appendix E, the USAF EOD force has the following capabilities:

(1)   Launch and Recovery of Aircraft. The USAF's EOD teams directly support sortie generation. They respond to airfield emergencies according to peacetime requirements of safety, resource protection, and sound judgment. Wartime operations involving aircraft differ from peacetime operations primarily from an increased operations tempo.

(2)   Force Protection. To provide a secure environment, USAF EOD operations require EOD forces to respond outside traditional base boundaries. AF EOD plays a critical role in force protection by eliminating or mitigating explosive hazards created by known or suspected criminal and terrorist devices.

(3)   Airfield Recovery Operations. CE rapid runway repair includes EOD operations during airfield recovery operations. The SRC plans, prioritizes, and controls all airfield recovery operations. The SRC integrates all assets (to include engineer, EOD, security forces, disaster preparedness, communications, transportation, resource management) to support postattack recovery operations.

(4)   Aerial Port Operations. Aerial ports are vital links to transportation in both surge and sustainment operations. They are susceptible targets for hostile forces wishing to disrupt operations. They have a substantial EOD mission relative to the increased movement of munitions. Additionally, enemy ordnance captured for intelligence assessment must transit these ports.

(5)   Mortuary Services. Because of ordnance being left on or imbedded in casualties, processing casualty operations should involve EOD teams. While this is particularly important at the CONUS-port mortuaries (last military involvement prior to turning over casualties to the families), EOD teams should also support theater mortuary efforts.

(6)   Base Populace Training. AF EOD personnel provide training on ordnance hazards and recognition, mine awareness, terrorist bomb search and recognition procedures, and personnel protective measures.

(7)   DS Units (Full Capability Nuclear Support). The AF assigns EOD personnel dealing with nuclear munitions in personnel reliability program positions. The program is set up to review the individual's background prior to working with nuclear munitions. Personnel working in DS units with full capability nuclear support train to perform all necessary EOD actions on nuclear weapon systems from site stabilization to site recovery.

6. Training

a.   "SILVER FLAG". This exercise prepares EOD forces for airfield operations in MTW environments via classroom, practical hands-on exercises, and field training. The SILVER FLAG course/exercise provides classroom and practice training in the following areas:

(1) Force protection planning.

(2) Large vehicle operations.

(3) NBC operations.

(4) IED tools and procedures.

(5) ARTS.

(6) Portable radio communications-139 radio system.

(7) Land navigation.

(8) Global positioning system.

(9) Damage assessment operations.

(10) Standoff munitions disruption.

(11) Minefield operations.

The first three days of training are classroom and practical, culminating with an integrated airfield recovery exercise. The exercise is based on a humanitarian/MOOTW scenario that allows students to apply skills learned throughout the course in a realistic environment.

b. Air Mobility Warfare Center-"PHOENIX READINESS". The Air Mobility Warfare Center conducts a training event for EOD forces (also known as Exercise PHOENIX READINESS). The exercise prepares EOD forces for MOOTW environments via classroom, practical, and field training. The training culminates in a four-day deployment exercise.

MULTISERVICE EOD CAPABILITIES MATRIX

Capability	Army			Navy					Air Force		Marine Corps			
	EOD Team	EOD Company	CONUS Support Company	Mobile	MCM	VSW/MCM	Shore	OCD	Home Base	Deployed	MEU	ESB EOD Platoon	MWSS EOD Section	Base/Station
CONVENTIONAL MUNITIONS														
Locate/Identify	X	X	X	X	X		X	X	X	X	X	X	X	X
Render Safe Procedures (RSP)	X	X	X	X	X		X		X	X	X	X	X	X
Dispose	X	X	X	X	X		X	X	X	X	X	X	X	X
Near-Surface Buried Munition Detection	X	X	X	X	X		X	X	X	X	X	X	X	X
Subsurface Buried Munition Detection	X	X	X	X	X		X	X	X	X	X	X	X	X
Buried Ordnance Recovery	X	X	X	X	X		X	X	X	X	X	X	X	X
Large Area Munitions Clearance	X	X	X	X	X		X	X	X	X	X	X	X	X
Airfield Recovery		X	X	X	X		X	X	X	X	X	X	X	X
Submunitions Clearance	X	X	X	X	X		X	X	X	X	X	X	X	X
Surface Munitions Disruption	X	X	X	X	X		X		X	X	X	X	X	X
Munitions Storage Area Accident Cleanup		X	X	X	X		X		X	X	X	X	X	X

Capability	Army			Navy					Air Force		Marine Corps			
	EOD Team	EOD Company	CONUS Support Company	Mobile	MCM	VSW/MCM	Shore	OCD	Home Base	Deployed	MEU	ESB EOD Platoon	MWSS EOD Section	Base/Station
Naval Sea Mines (1)														
Locate/Identify				X	X	X	X	X						
RSP				X	X	X	X							
Dispose				X	X	X	X	X						
Recover					X									
Low-Influence Diving				X	X	X	X(3)	X(3)						
Limpet Mines (1)														
Locate/Identify				X	X		X	X						
RSP				X	X		X							
Dispose				X	X		X	X						
UNDERWATER ORDNANCE (1)														
Locate/Identify				X	X	X	X	X						
RSP				X	X	X	X							
Dispose				X	X	X	X	X						
IED	X	X	X	X	X		X		X	X	X	X	X	X
Large Vehicle IED	X	X	X	X	X		X		X	X	X	X	X	X
WMD (2)														
Locate/Identify	X	X	X	X			X(3)		X(3)	X(3)	X(3)	X(3)	X(3)	X(3)
RSP		X(3)		X			X							
NUCLEAR MUNITIONS														
Radiation Detection/Monitor	X	X	X	X			X(3)		X		X	X	X	X
RSP Nuclear System				X			X(3)		X			X	X	X

Capability	Army			Navy					Air Force		Marine Corps			
	EOD Team	EOD Company	CONUS Support Company	Mobile	MCM	VSW/MCM	Shore	OCD	Home Base	Deployed	MEU	ESB EOD Platoon	MWSS EOD Section	Base/Station
Continue RSP				X(3)			X(3)		X			X	X	X
Seal/Package			X	X			X(3)		X		X	X	X	X
BIOLOGICAL MUNITIONS														
Detection														
Decontaminate	X	X	X	X			X(3)							
Seal/Package				X	X	X	X(3)		X					
RSP					X		X(3)		X	X	X	X	X	X
Emergency Disposal				X	X	X	X(3)		X	X	X	X	X	X
CHEMICAL MUNITIONS														
Agent Identification	X	X	X	X	X		X(3)		X	X	X	X	X	X
Agent Decontamination	X	X	X	X	X		X(3)		X	X	X	X	X	X
Seal/Package	X	X	X	X			X(3)		X	X	X	X	X	X
RSP	X	X	X	X			X(3)		X	X	X	X	X	X
Emergency Disposal	X	X	X	X	X		X(3)		X	X	X	X	X	X
Munitions Intel Gathering	X	X	X	X	X	X	X	X	X	X	X	X	X	X
Exploitation				X	X	X	X		X	X	X	X	X	X
Inerting											X	X	X	X
Explosive Demolition	X	X	X	X	X	X	X	X	X	X	X	X	X	X
Vessel Boarding Search & Seizure				X	X						X			
NEO	X	X	X	X	X		X(3)			X	X	X	X	

Capability	Army			Navy					Air Force		Marine Corps			
	EOD Team	EOD Company	CONUS Support Company	Mobile	MCM	VSW/MCM	Shore	OCD	Home Base	Deployed	MEU	ESB EOD Platoon	MWSS EOD Section	Base/Station
TRAP/Combat Search and Rescue				X	X		X(3)				X	X	X	
Aircraft Crash Recovery	X	X	X	X(4)	X(4)		X(4)	X(4)	X	X	X	X	X	X
VIP Protection	X	X	X	X	X		X		X	X	X	X	X	X
Dynamic Entry	X(5)	X(5)	X(5)	X(5)	X(5)		X(5)				X(5)	X(5)	X(5)	X(5)
Tactical Insert/Extract Personnel and Equipment														
Parachute				X(6)			X(6)				X			
SPIE				X	X		X				X	X	X	X
Fastrope				X	X		X				X	X	X	X
Rappel				X	X		X				X	X	X	X
CRRC				X			X							
Casting				X	X	X	X	X						
Robotics (Small)							X		X	X				
Robotics (Large)		X	X						X	X			X	X
Satellite Communications				X	X	X	X	X		X	X			
Organic Tactical Communications	X	X	X	X	X	X	X	X	X	X	X	X	X	

(1) In water only, otherwise treat as conventional ordnance.
(2) Refer to established OPLANS for further guidance.
(3) Selected detachments only.
(4) Includes in-water recovery.
(5) See service chapters for unique breaching capabilities.
(6) Only designated Mobile and shore detachments.

Appendix B

EOD PLANNING CHECKLIST
FOR JOINT OPERATIONS

1. Mobilization Planning

   a. Train, equip, and organize EOD forces within
each service component. _____

   b. Review OPLANs for EOD requirements and the
planned flow of EOD forces time-phased forces
deployment list (TPFDL). _____

   c. Consider adding an EOD-qualified officer to the
combatant commander's special staff. _____

   d. Identify opportunities for joint EOD operations in
exercise plan (EXPLANs), OPLANs, CONPLANs,
and OPORDs. _____

   e. Perform an intelligence estimate of information
necessary to counter the UXO and IED threat
including: _____

      (1) Ordnance orders of battle.

      (2) Terrorist/paramilitary threats and capabilities.

      (3) Critical target listing (enemy) and munitions
US forces plan to use.

      (4) Critical vulnerabilities (friendly) and what
munitions the enemy may use.

   f. Coordinate periodic joint, interoperability
exercises with multiservice EOD forces. _____

2. Deployment Planning

   a. Update intelligence estimate. _____

   b. Update mission analysis to determine EOD
requirements to support the mission, to include— _____

      (1) joint EOD mission requirements.

      (2) service EOD requirements.

      (3) total EOD requirements.

c. Source the EOD requirements to support joint and service-specific missions. _____

d. Determine flow of EOD forces (TPFDL). _____

3. Employment Planning

a. Develop mission statements and concept of operations. _____

    (1) Identify single-service EOD missions (See Chapters III-VI).

    (2) Identify joint EOD missions (See Chapter II).

    (3) Select employment options for conducting joint operations (See Chapter II).

        (a) Service responsibility with DIRLAUTH.

        (b) Lead service component (with or without TACON/OPCON).

        (c) Subordinate JEODTF.

b. Establish JEODOC (if required) (See Chapter II and Appendix C). _____

c. Ensure methodology is in place for intelligence collection and dissemination. _____

    (1) Disseminate new or unknown ordnance technical information within theater.

    (2) Process new or unknown ordnance items to appropriate agencies outside theater.

    (3) Coordinate with the National Imagery and Mapping Agency for updated mapping, geodesy, and multispectral imagery data covering the area of the UXO/EOD incident.

4. Sustainment Planning

a. Coordinate administrative and logistical support with Theater Support Command or service components. _____

b. Monitor EOD reports; take action as required. _____

5. Redeployment Planning

   a. Ensure EOD commanders understand and
employ appropriate procedures (for instance,
explosives safety and environmental protection)
for the closing of demolition areas.   _____

   b. Establish EOD battle hand-off requirements and
procedures—   _____

     (1) to host nation.

     (2) to coalition EOD forces.

     (3) to civilian contractors.

   c. Determine redeployment flow of EOD forces.   _____

   d. Conduct post-mission analysis.   _____

Appendix C

ESTABLISHING A JEODTF

1. Background

A key responsibility of the geographic combatant commander is the designation of an EOD controlling authority after a full evaluation of the assigned mission. It is important for the efficiency of the TF that the JEODTF J-3 is a currently qualified EOD officer. All personnel assigned to the JEODTF staff should understand multiservice or joint TTP to allow for a seamless transition. JEODTF planning should be in concert with established joint doctrine as found in JP 5-00.2, *Joint Task Force Planning Guidance Procedures.*

2. Authority

Establishment of a JEODTF is appropriate when EOD C^2 requirements exceed the capabilities of the theater EOD staff or when conducting EOD operations with a joint force would be more efficient. The CJTF normally forms a JEODTF from the nucleus of the designated major service component EOD command. Both the Army and Navy have existing C^2 EOD units around which a JEODTF is built. Specifically, using the Army's EOD group (0-6 command) headquarters, or the Navy's mobile group (0-6 command), provides a ready EOD headquarters unit to serve as a building block for a JEODTF headquarters. A combatant commander establishes and deploys a JEODTF from outside the theater of operations. When formed, the JEODTF is a temporary joint EOD headquarters that controls two or more different service component's EOD units in a specific JOA to accomplish the EOD mission. The JEODTF supports the theater campaign plan, JTF mission, or other operations as directed.

3. Responsibilities

The JEODTF is responsible for making recommendations to the CJTF (or geographic combatant commander if a JTF has not been formed) on the proper employment of EOD and for accomplishing assigned operational missions. The JEODTF develops a detailed plan using the JOPES for integrated employment of assigned and attached forces based on an assessment of the operational requirements.

a. Organization of Forces. The commander, JEODTF, has the authority to organize assigned or attached forces to meet mission requirements.

b.   Commander's Guidance. The combatant commander is responsible for—

(1)   defining the scope of responsibility of the JEODTF.

(2)   defining units assigned OPCON, TACON, and relationships within the JFC.

(3)   defining JEODTF AORs for force protection, UXO response, and other missions.

(4)   ensuring that all identified external support requirements for sustaining the EOD force are properly coordinated.

4. The JEODTF Staff

The designated EOD commander coordinates the establishment of the JEODTF staff. A doctrinal method is to develop JEODTF staffs around the "core" of the designated EOD commander's assigned staff. Other service EOD personnel augment the designated JEODTF's core staff. The geographic combatant commander may also provide certain augmentation (to include security, medical, and administration/logistics) to a JEODTF, depending on the mission and support requirements. See Figure C-1, Notional JEODTF Staff Organization.

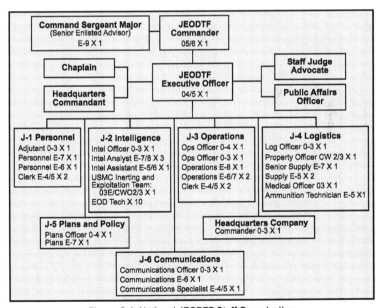

Figure C-1. Notional JEODTF Staff Organization

a. Organization. EOD commanders organize the JEODTF staff as necessary to carry out assigned duties and responsibilities. The JEODTF staff includes at a minimum the normal J-1 through J-4 staff and may include J-5 and J-6 as well as special staff members as required.

b. Orientation Program. A staff orientation program ensures that all individuals assigned to the JEODTF become thoroughly familiar with multiservice and joint EOD operations. This can be accomplished through the establishment of a joint reception center, a short training program, or even use of a "buddy" system whereby an experienced JEODTF staff member mentors a newly assigned individual.

5. Staff Functions and Responsibilities

a. The Manpower and Personnel Directorate (J-1). The J-1 provides joint personnel planning, coordination, management, and review; assists subordinate commands in acquiring, replacing, and transferring personnel; provides administrative and personnel service; monitors and reports the personnel readiness of assigned, allocated, and apportioned forces to higher headquarters; and provides appropriate input to OPLANs.

b. The Intelligence Directorate (J-2). The primary function of the J-2 is to support the JEODTF staff and subordinate assigned/attached units by ensuring the availability of reliable intelligence and timely indications and warning on the characteristics of UXO on the battlefield, first-seen ordnance, and potential terrorist threats. Members of the directorate actively participate in joint staff planning and in planning, coordinating, directing, integrating, and controlling a concentration of intelligence efforts on the proper enemy items-of-intelligence interest at the appropriate time. The J-2 also has the functional responsibility for the acquisition, production, requests, and dissemination of intelligence and counterintelligence to support EOD operations. The J-2 develops, refines, and updates the JEODTF intelligence estimate to provide a common understanding and view of the battlefield and directs intelligence collection efforts and exploitation of first-seen/recovered foreign ordnance. The J-2 serves as the single POC within intelligence channels for the collection and dissemination of technical intelligence products and provides intelligence input to OPORDs.

c. The Operations Directorate (J-3). The J-3 plans, coordinates, and integrates EOD operations with that of the supported commander. Should the JEODTF not include a J-5, the J-3 would also perform long-range or future planning functions. The J-3 conducts crisis action planning; assists the J-5 (if organized) in deliberate planning; and coordinates and directs the deployment, employment, and redeployment of assigned and attached forces. The J-3 is responsible for providing oversight of current operations and planning for emerging missions; maintaining a current operations estimate; preparing operational plans, annexes, orders, reports, and records; determining pre-deployment technical training requirements for replacement EOD personnel; and recommending EOD priorities for operational support, task organization, and JTF boundaries. Should the JEODTF not include a J-6, the J-3 would also perform the C^4I planning and execution functions.

d. The Logistics Directorate (J-4). The J-4 formulates logistics plans and coordinates supply, maintenance, transportation, field services, general engineering, health services, contracting, host-nation support, and other logistics activities. The J-4 provides logistic oversight for JEODTF and the management of external logistics.

e. The Plans Directorate (J-5). The J-5 conducts deliberate planning for the JEODTF, develops and recommends C^2 arrangements, and participates in the JTF, theater, or combatant command's campaign and concept planning. The J-5 also projects future EOD requirements for personnel, material, and organization. When required, the J-5 provides the JEODTF input for the JOPES.

f. The C^4I Systems Directorate (J-6). The J-6 is responsible for communications, electronics, and automated information systems in support of the JEODTF. This includes development and integration of C^4I architecture and plans that support the command's operational and strategic requirements as well as policy and guidance for implementation and integration of interoperable C^4I systems to exercise command in the execution of the JEODTF mission.

g. Staff Judge Advocate (SJA). The SJA is the legal advisor on issues ranging from administrative law to rules of engagement. To ensure the JEODTF complies with international law, domestic law, environmental protection laws, and DOD regulations, the SJA coordinates with the JTF SJA and JEODTF supported commands.

h. Public Affairs Officer (PAO). The PAO advises the JEODTF commander on public opinion pertaining to the impact of EOD operations, public affairs policy and guidance from higher headquarters, and the command's need to establish a detailed media communications plan. The media communications plan focuses on providing overarching public affairs guidance on media relationships, targeting internal and external audiences, providing key messages, and detailing the production of public information materials (to include web pages, fact sheets, releases, and related materials). Finally, the PAO serves as the JEODTF spokesperson and ensures that the public affairs portion of EXPLANs, CONPLANs, OPLANs, and OPORDs, and related planning and execution documents are properly prepared and coordinated

i. Chaplain. The chaplain is the JEODTF commander's primary staff officer in the areas of religion, morals, and morale as affected by religion. The chaplain is the commander's adviser on indigenous religions and local religious practices. They provide religious support to all TF members regardless of service.

j.   HQ Commandant. The commander, JEODTF, appoints the HQ commandant, who is responsible for all aspects of the headquarters operation. The commandant assumes the initial functional responsibility for all equipment and facilities assigned to the JEODTF and assigns subsequent functions to personnel and agencies in direct control of those activities. The commander must include the HQ commandant in the JEODTF planning process to fully support the efforts of the EOD mission.

STANDARDIZED EOD REPORTS

1. Background

Timely and accurate UXO reporting and intelligence information gathering during EOD operations, regardless of service component, is critical to the safe conduct of operations within an AOR. Although reporting procedures are similar between the service components and provide similar information, submission and dissemination procedures differ. Timely, standardized reporting and dissemination provide multiservice EOD forces with the ability to effectively counter the hazards associated with ordnance. During multiservice operations, using the following reports prevents redundancy and ensures accurate EOD incident tasking, reporting, and tracking.

2. UXO Spot Report

a. Purpose. The UXO Spot Report is a detailed, two-way reporting system that makes clear where the UXO hazard areas are, the priority for clearance, and which units the hazard affects. The report is used to request help in handling a UXO hazard that affects the unit's mission and is beyond their ability to handle. This report helps the commander set priorities based on the battlefield situation. The UXO Spot Report is the first echelon report sent when an observer detects UXO. The report consists of nine lines and is sent by the fastest means available. See Table D-1, Sample UXO Spot Report.

b. Routing. Forward the UXO Spot Report through the chain of command. Each commander in the chain who reviews the report may change the priority to reflect the current tactical situation or projected battle plans. Each commander in the chain is responsible for forwarding UXO Spot Reports through command channels and for setting the proper priority for each report. A higher-level commander in the chain that changes a priority must inform subordinate commands, especially the initial reporting unit. In addition to the priority status, all commanders need to be kept informed of the status of each UXO hazard in their area. The reporting unit's higher headquarters that is supported by EOD or engineer forces determines the final priority. Based on METT-T, with the Army adding a "C" for civilian considerations, EOD teams use the UXO spot reports to prioritize and sequence their response to assigned UXO incidents.

Table D-1. Sample UXO Spot Report

Line 1.	Date-Time Group (DTG): DTG item was discovered.
Line 2.	Reporting Activity (unit identification code and location (grid of UXO).
Line 3.	Contact Method: Radio frequency, call sign, POC, and telephone number.
Line 4.	Type of Ordnance: Dropped, projected, placed, or thrown. If available, give the size of the hazard area and number of items, if more than one. Without touching, disturbing, or approaching (due to a potential tripwire) the item, include details about size, shape, color, and condition (intact or leaking).
Line 5.	NBC Contamination: Be as specific as possible.
Line 6.	Resources Threatened: Report any equipment, facilities, or other assets that are threatened.
Line 7.	Impact on Mission: Provide a short description of your current tactical situation and how the presence of the UXO affects your status.
Line 8.	Protective Measures: Describe any measures taken to protect personnel and equipment.
Line 9.	Recommended Priority: Recommend a priority for response by EOD technicians or engineers.
Priority	**Basis**
Immediate	Stops the unit's maneuver and mission capability, or threatens critical assets vital to the mission.
Indirect	Slows the unit's maneuver and mission capability, or threatens critical assets important to the mission.
Minor	Reduces the unit's maneuver and mission capability, or threatens noncritical assets of value.
No Threat	Has little or no affect on the unit's capabilities or assets.

3. EOD Incident Report

The EOD unit responding to the incident submits this report in message, memorandum, or digital format. See Table D-2 for the format of the EOD incident report. The EOD unit should immediately report essential details of the operation that have immediate and vital significance. Include the following relevant information in the EOD incident report.

Table D-2. Sample EOD Incident Report

Line 1.	Responding EOD unit.
Line 2.	Personnel, vehicles, and any special equipment responding to incident.
Line 3.	Site POC or on-scene commander.
Line 4.	Geographical location (latitude/longitude and/or Global Positioning System) and location with respect to buildings or valuable installations.
Line 5.	Chronological record of operations, including safety precautions taken.
Line 6.	Detailed description and available photographs/drawings of items; positive identification; external markings/condition of case or body; worn or damaged parts; corrosion; extent and kind of sea growth; condition of explosives; fuzing/firing mechanisms; batteries; important components or fittings; and antistripping devices or booby traps.
Line 7.	Reason object failed to function as designed.
Line 8.	Difficulties or unusual circumstances related to the incident.
Line 9.	RSP used, if applicable.
Line 10.	Final disposition of items.
Line 11.	List expenditure of demolition materials.
Line 12.	Additional pertinent information.

NOTE: This report does not supersede, unless specified, specific service reporting requirements.

4. Technical Intelligence Reports.

Technical intelligence reporting follows the appropriate service procedures contained in Army technical manual/Air Force Technical Order/Navy EOD Bulletin 60A-1-1-7.

5. Lead Service and JEODTF EOD Report.

Each service maintains unique, service-specific EOD reports and formats. It is useful when conducting operations as a joint force to have mutual reports and reporting formats. Those EOD assets under TACON/OPCON of lead service or JEODTF prepare the following intelligence reports for first-seen ordnance:

a. Spot Report. The acquiring unit prepares the spot report as an oral or written report. The sender transmits the report by the fastest means available. The minimum information requirements for this report are as follows:

(1) Identification of reporting unit.

(2) What is being reported (for instance ordnance or documents).

(3) Time and location of recovery.

(4) Quantity of material.

(5) Condition of material.

(6) POC.

b. Preliminary Technical Report (PRETECHREP) Type B. See Table D-3, Sample PRETECHREP. An EOD unit forwards this report when an item of ordnance has technical intelligence value. The sender of the report forwards the report to the JEODOC/JEODTF J-2. An interim RSP is developed and reported, whether the RSP is issued or not.

Table D-3. Sample PRETECHREP

For the protection of sources and methods and unless otherwise directed by on-scene intelligence personnel, the initial report shall be classified SECRET/ NOFORN/WNINTEL. WARNING NOTICE – INTELLIGENCE SOURCES OR METHODS INVOLVED. The first paragraph of the report shall read: 1. (U) This report is initially classified S/NF/WNINTEL for protection of sources and methods. Verification of correct classification by (your service intelligence organization) is required.
Foreign nuclear weapons or components, including sabotage devices, are evacuated through technical intelligence channels. Security classification of such items, once in evacuation channels, will not be lower than SECRET (RESTRICTED DATA).
PRIORITY FM: XXXX ORD CO (EOD) TO: XXXX (JEODOC) INFO: CDRUSATECHDET INDIAN HEAD MD NAVEODTECHDIV INDIAN HEAD MD// FSTC CHARLOTTESVILLE VA//AIFRCB/AIFIM// DIA WASHINGTON DC//DT2C/DT-3B// BT SECRET/NOFORN/WNINTEL WARNING NOTICE - SENSITIVE INTELLIGENCE SOURCES OR METHODS INVOLVED

Table D-3. Sample PRETECHREP (continued)

SUBJ: PRETECHREP

REF   A. MSG XXX SUBJECT: SPOT REPORT

a. ( ) DATE FOUND, LOCATION (map references)
b. ( ) TYPE OF EQUIPMENT AND QUANTITY
c. ( ) ORIGIN
d. ( ) BRIEF DESCRIPTION WITH DISTINGUISHING MARKS
e. ( ) TECHNICAL CHARACTERISTICS WITH AN IMMEDIATE VALUE
f.   ( ) NAME OF COMMANDER OF CAPTURING UNIT
g. ( ) TIME AND ORIGIN OF MESSAGE
h. ( ) TENTATIVE RSP (EOD use only)

(Classification)

NOTE: The subject and each paragraph and subparagraph must be classified individually, but not higher than the classification of the entire message.

Examples: 1. (Secret/No-Foreign); 2. (Unclassified)

c.   Complementary Technical Report (COMTECHREP) Type B.

(1)   Purpose. Use the COMTECHREP Type B to report information about explosive ordnance. Technical intelligence (TECHINT) teams prepare these reports, as do EOD personnel. However, EOD personnel only prepare them in the absence of a TECHINT team or when requested by a G-2 or representative. This report must be as complete and detailed as possible. EOD personnel prepare and send this report by the fastest means through the JEODOC/JEODTF J-2 to the TECHINT unit.

(2)   Timing and Completeness. Complete all of the items in the report that you have information for and strive for the most complete report possible. However, when a detailed report might result in serious delay and the report is of significant or new items of extreme urgency, complete only paragraphs a-e, l(1), y, and aa of priority message. See Table D-4, Sample COMTECHREP.

(3)   Additional Information. Additional paragraphs of particular importance, for example, those referring to safety (paragraph u) or design (paragraph m) may be included at the originator's discretion. Paragraph aa should state an estimated time required for a detailed report to be completed.

Table D-4. Sample COMTECHREP

PRIORITY

FM: XXXX ORD CO (EOD)
TO: XXXX (JEODOC)
INFO: CDRUSATECHDET INDIAN HEAD MD
NAVEODTECHCEN INDIAN HEAD MD//DC//
FSTC CHARLOTTESVILLE VA//AIFRCB/AIFIM//
DIA WASHINGTON DC//DT2C/DT-3B//

BT
SECRET/NOFORN/WNINTEL
WARNING NOTICE - SENSITIVE INTELLIGENCE SOURCES OR
METHODS INVOLVED

SUBJ: COMTECHREP
REF A. MSG XXX SUBJECT: PRETECHREP

a. Date and location of acquisition, acquired by, and for whom.
b. Nationality, designation, and identification marks.
c. Description.
d. Overall length, including fuze, tail, vanes, or control surfaces and fittings; measurement of various states (if there are several).
e. Maximum diameter of each state (if there are several).
f. Shape, design, and internal configuration (streamlining shells).
g. Span of vanes and control surfaces.
h. Number, relative positions, and dimensions (width, length, size, and/or configuration of control surfaces).
i. Thickness of casing at—
   (1) nose.
   (2) slides.
   (3) base.
j. Type and materials of body and control surfaces.
k. Color and markings of—
   (1) nose.
   (2) body.
   (3) tail and vanes.
l. Weight—
   (1) total, including propellant.
   (2) of filling.
m. Nature of filling. If chemical or biological warfare in nature, give method of filling, for example, bomblets or massive fill; specify method of delivery, such as spray, groundburst, or airburst. For antitank missiles with high-explosive, antitank (HEAT) warheads, give full details of cone-liner materials, cone angle, and diameter. For antitank missiles with non-HEAT warheads, give full description of the warhead.

Table D-4. Sample COMTECHREP (continued)

n. Type of missile guidance system and method of stabilization environment (control and guidance radars, acquisition radar); frequencies used for reception response (in case of a transponder); and proximity fuze (if there is one). Electronic countermeasures and electronic counter-countermeasures equipment and/or chaff-dispensing equipment.

o. Sensors.

p. Diameter of radome and size of homing dish, if fitted.

q. Dimensions (internal and external) of wave guides in the homing head, and wave guides and or aerials in the wings or body, and the technology used.

r. Homing head, transducer design, and shape and size (torpedoes).

s. Method of propulsion and propeller data (torpedoes).

t. Detonating system, fuzing system (nose, tail, or transverse) and firing mechanism details.

u. Type of suspension, giving details of devices used, such as electrically operated hoods or release gear.

v. Antihandling or booby-trap devices.

w. Other information (to include estimate of time required to prepare item for shipment to TECHINT center or designated industrial firm for detailed analysis).

x. Name of officer in command of technical team making examination.

y. Time and origin of message.

z. Energy used for mobile systems other than propulsions.

aa. Estimate of time required for completion.

Note: If feasible, a preliminary set of photographs should be sent with the report.

(Classification)

Note: The subject and each paragraph and subparagraph must be classified individually, but not higher than the classification of the entire message. Examples: 1. (S/NF); a. (U); b. (C).

6. Responsibilities

a. Service Responsibility (with DIRLAUTH). DIRLAUTH as authorized by CJTF allows for more rapid dissemination of ordnance intelligence between service EOD forces prior to submitting reports into intelligence channels. Each service EOD command must coordinate with other EOD assets to disseminate this information.

b. JEODOC. The JEODOC, when established, is responsible for the collection of incident tracking reports and ordnance intelligence from service-component EOD assets, assessment and dissemination of information to all service EOD assets within the AO, and submission of consolidated information reports to intelligence channels.

    c.   JEODTF. The JEODTF collects incident tracking reports and ordnance intelligence from service-component EOD assets, assesses and disseminates information to all service EOD assets within the AO, and submits consolidated information reports to intelligence channels.

EOD Recurring Support Operations

1. Background

The DOD EOD force performs numerous support missions on a recurring basis. Each of the services EOD personnel assists in the performance of these missions.

2. Recurring DOD EOD Support Missions

The DOD EOD force performs the following missions on a recurring basis:

a. VIPPSA.

(1) General. Currently the DOS and DOD use joint EOD assets to support the USSS and the DOS in protecting the President or Vice President and their immediate families (as defined by DOD Instruction 5030.34). This protection is also provided to the US Secretary of State, foreign heads of state, prime ministers, ministers of defense, or other VIPs as specified by the President of the United States. The EOD force provides specific protection from all potentially hazardous explosive devices within assigned secure areas for protecting VIPs.

(2) Executive Agent. The Secretary of the Army is the DOD executive agent for the direct receipt, approval, coordination, and tasking of USSS and DOS requests for routine reimbursable and nonreimbursable EOD protective support for locations worldwide. The Assistant Secretary of the Army (Installations, Logistics, and Environment) maintains oversight of this support on behalf of the executive agent. The Director of Military Support provides staff support to the Secretary of the Army to assist in carrying out this executive agency. Commander, US Joint Forces Command (USJFCOM), is designated the operating agent to act on behalf of the executive agent to plan, coordinate, task, and execute routine EOD VIP protective support employing assets from the military services and the unified and specified commands. The US Army EOD for VIPPSA, Fort Gillem, GA, is the tasking and coordinating agent for the Commander, USJFCOM.

(3) CONUS and Outside the Continental US (OCONUS) Missions. Support requests from USSS or DOS are communicated directly to the VIPPSA. For missions within CONUS, the VIPPSA identifies the closest EOD unit (of any service) and tasks that unit's command to provide EOD teams to support the USSS or DOS security details. For OCONUS missions, the VIPPSA tasks the geographical combatant commander to provide EOD teams. EOD teams assigned to support USSS or DOS are subject to overall supervision and direction of the USSS Director or the Director of the DOS

Office of Diplomatic Security (or their authorized representative) at the mission site for the duration of the support mission.

    (4)   VIPPSA Tasks. A typical EOD VIP support mission will include the following tasks:

        (a) Conduct a site survey of areas to be visited by the protectee.

        (b) Assist in establishing evacuation routes for potentially hazardous explosive devices.

        (c) Search the areas to be visited by the protectee for hazardous explosive devices.

        (d) Clear the protectees' departure route in the event a hazardous explosive device is discovered.

    (5)   If the EOD team discovers a hazardous explosive device, provide technical assistance to local law enforcement agencies/bomb disposal teams as requested.

    b.   Force Protection. Since criminal and terrorist attacks commonly involve the use of explosive devices on US forces, force commanders should include EOD commanders/planners in all force protection planning and training. During periods of conflict, the awareness of, and emphasis on, force protection are heightened, thus increasing EOD response to potentially hazardous situations. In addition to actual response to explosive devices, EOD forces can provide training in UXO/IED recognition and reporting; bomb threat search procedures and evacuation; site vulnerability assessments, and SOP preparation and validation. This training will increase the effectiveness of the commander's force protection program. EOD forces also provide DS to NEO forces.

    c.   Joint Task Force Full Accounting (JTFFA). JTFFA is a standing task force under the Commander in Chief, Pacific (CINCPAC). EOD personnel support the JTFFA by providing the fullest possible accounting of US personnel listed as missing in action in Vietnam, Cambodia, and Laos. Most sites investigated by JTFFA teams are littered with UXO from military action, or in the case of aircraft crash sites, from UXO that was part of the aircraft's payload. EOD personnel clear UXO from investigation sites so that JTFFA recovery personnel can operate in a safe environment. EOD support to this mission is provided by all services, and primarily from units within CINCPAC.

    d.   WMD. Certain EOD units have special capabilities and training to recognize and render safe all known types of WMD. All EOD units are trained to provide first response to suspected WMD and to assist in coordination of responses by more specialized national WMD response assets.

    e.   Intelligence Gathering and Reporting. EOD forces perform technical intelligence gathering and reporting on new or first-seen foreign ordnance, aircraft, weapons systems, or sabotage devices encountered by maneuver forces.

f.   HDO. EOD forces develop training programs and conduct HDO training in support of SOF in developing countries that are experiencing landmine/UXO problems.

g.   Weapon/Ammunition Storage Site Inspections. EOD forces conduct inspections of weapon/ammunition storage sites during peacekeeping operations for compliance with peace agreements. EOD forces assist with the safety and storage requirements for ammunition and associated components.

h.   Destruction of Foreign Ammunition. EOD forces inspect and destroy foreign ammunition and explosive items.

i.   Amnesty Programs. EOD units assist in the collection and disposal of hazardous munitions and components as part of the maneuver commander's force protection program to ensure the continued safety of military personnel.

j.   Accident/Incident Investigation. EOD forces provide technical information on foreign and US ordnance and conduct crater or munition fragmentation analysis, as part of an accident or incident investigation.

Glossary

PART I—ABBREVIATIONS AND ACRONYMS

A

ADCON	administrative control
admin	administrative
AF	Air Force
AFB	Air Force base
AFDC	Air Force Doctrine Center
AFFOR	Air Force forces
AFJI	Air Force Joint Instruction
AFTTP(I)	Air Force tactics, techniques, and procedures (interservice)
AL	Alabama
ALSA	Air Land Sea Application
AMCM	airborne mine countermeasures
AO	area of operations
AOR	area of responsibility
AR	Army regulation
ARFOR	Army forces
ARG	amphibious ready group
ARTS	all-purpose remote transport system
ASCC	Army service component commander
ASD	area search detachment
ATTN	attention
AZ	Arizona

B

BCE	base civil engineer
BEEF	base engineer emergency force

C

(C)	confidential
C²	command and control

C^4I	command, control, communications, computers, and intelligence
CA	California
CATF	commander, amphibious task force
CE	civil engineer
C-E	communications-electronics
CES	civil engineer squadron
CINC	commander in chief
CINCPAC	Commander in Chief, Pacific
CJTF	commander, joint task force
CO	Colorado
comm	commercial phone line
COMTECHREP	complementary technical report
CONPLAN	contingency plan
CONUS	continental United States
CRRC	combat rubber raiding craft
CVBG	carrier battle group

D

DA	Department of the Army
DC	District of Columbia
DIRLAUTH	direct liaison authorized
DOD	Department of Defense
DOS	Department of State
DS	direct support
DSN	Defense Switched Network
DTG	date-time group

E

E	enlisted (with number represents pay grade)
EAF	expeditionary airfield
EOD	explosive ordnance disposal
EODMU	explosive ordnance disposal mobile unit
EODTEU	explosive ordnance disposal training and evaluation unit
ESB	engineer support battalion
EXPLAN	exercise plan

F

FL	Florida
FM	field manual
FORSCOM	US Army Forces Command

G

G-2	Army or Marine Corps component intelligence staff officer
G-4	Army or Marine Corps component logistics staff officer
GA	Georgia
GOPLAT	gas and oil platform
GS	general support

H

H&S	headquarters and services
HA	humanitarian assistance
HDO	humanitarian demining operations
HEAT	high-explosive, antitank
HI	Hawaii
HMMWV	high-mobility multipurpose wheeled vehicle
HQ	headquarters

I

IED	improvised explosive device
IHR	in-extremous hostage recovery
IM	information management
intel	intelligence

J

J-1	manpower and personnel directorate of a joint staff
J-2	intelligence directorate of a joint staff
J-3	operations directorate of a joint staff
J-4	logistics directorate of a joint staff
J-5	plans directorate of a joint staff
J-6	command, control, communications, and computer systems directorate of a joint staff
JEODOC	joint explosive ordnance disposal operations center

JEODTF	joint explosive ordnance disposal task force
JFC	joint force commander
JFLCC	joint force land component commander
JOA	joint operations area
JOPES	Joint Operation Planning and Execution System
JP	joint pub
JSOTF	joint special operations task force
JTF	joint task force
JTFFA	joint task force full accounting

L

LNO	liaison officer
log	logistics

M

MAGTF	Marine air-ground task force
MAJCOM	major command
MARFOR	Marine forces
MCAS	Marine Corps air stations
MCCDC	Marine Corps Combat Development Command
MCD	mobile communications detachment
MCM	mine countermeasures
MCO	Marine Corps order
MCRP	Marine Corps reference publication
MCWP	Marine Corps warfighting publication
MD	Maryland
MDSU	mobile diving and salvage units
MEF	Marine expeditionary force
METT-T	mission, enemy, terrain and weather, troops and support available, time available
METT-TC	mission, enemy, terrain, troops, time available, and civilian constraints (Army only)
MEU	Marine expeditionary unit
MEU(SOC)	Marine expeditionary unit (special operations capable)
MIO	maritime intercept operation
MK	mark

MMS	Marine mammal system
MO	Missouri
MOB	mobile
MOD	module
MOOTW	military operation other than war
MP	military police
MSPF	maritime special purpose force
MSSG	Marine expeditionary unit service support group
MTTP	multiservice tactics, techniques, and procedures
MTW	major theater war
MWSS	Marine wing support squadron

N

NAVEODTECHDIV	Navy EOD technology division
NAVSCOLEOD	naval school explosive ordnance disposal
NBC	nuclear, biological, chemical
NAVFOR	Navy forces
NC	North Carolina
NCA	National Command Authority
NEO	noncombatant evacuation operations
NF	no-foreign (as in secret, no foreign)
NOFORN	no-foreign (as in secret, no foreign)
NRF	naval reserve force
NWDC	Navy Warfare Development Command
NWP	Navy warfare publication

O

O	officer (with number represents pay grade)
OCD	ordnance clearance detachment
OCONUS	outside the continental US
OH	Ohio
OPCON	operational control
OPLAN	operation plan
OPNAVINST	chief of naval operations instruction

OPORD	operation order
ops	operations

P

PAO	public affairs office
POC	point of contact
PRETECHREP	preliminary technical report

R

RI	Rhode Island
RSP	render safe procedures

S

(S)	secret
S-1	battalion or brigade personnel staff officer (Army; Marine Corps battalion, brigade, or regiment)
S-2	battalion or brigade intelligence staff officer (Army; Marine Corps battalion, brigade, or regiment)
S-3	battalion or brigade operations staff officer (Army; Marine Corps battalion, brigade, or regiment)
S-4	battalion or brigade logistics staff officer (Army; Marine Corps battalion, brigade, or regiment)
SC	South Carolina
SCUBA	self-contained underwater breathing apparatus
SHORE	shore-based (detachment)
SJA	staff judge advocate
SMCM	surface mine countermeasures
SOC	special operations capable
SOF	special operations forces
SOP	standard operating procedure
SPIE	specialized personnel insertion/extraction
SRC	survival recovery center

T

TACON	tactical control
TECHINT	technical intelligence
TF	task force

TPFDL	time-phased force deployment listing
TRADOC	US Army Training and Doctrine Command
TRAP	tactical recovery of aircraft or personnel
TTP	tactics, techniques, and procedures
TX	Texas

U

(U)	unclassified
UA-HMMWV	up-armored high-mobility multipurpose wheeled vehicle
UBA	underwater breathing apparatus
UMCM	underwater mine countermeasures
US	United States
USAF	US Air Force
USJFCOM	US Joint Forces Command
USMC	US Marine Corps
USN	US Navy
USSS	United States Secret Service
UT	Utah
UTC	unit type codes
UXO	unexploded explosive ordnance

V

VA	Virginia
VBSS	visit, board, search, and seize
VIP	very important person
VIPPSA	very important person protection support activity
VSW	very shallow water

W

WA	Washington
WMD	weapons of mass destruction
WW	world war

PART II—TERMS AND DEFINITIONS

administrative control. Direction or exercise of authority over subordinate or other organizations in respect to administration and support. It includes organization of service forces, control of resources and equipment, personnel management, unit logistics, individual and unit training, readiness, mobilization, demobilization, discipline, and other matters not included in the operational missions of the subordinate or other organizations. Also called **ADCON**.

area of operations. An operational area defined by the JFC for land and naval forces. Areas of operation do not typically encompass the entire operational area of the JFC, but should be large enough for component commanders to accomplish their missions and protect their forces. Also called **AO**.

area of responsibility. (1) The geographical area associated with a COCOM within which a combatant commander has authority to plan and conduct operations. (2) In naval usage, a predefined area of enemy terrain for which supporting ships are responsible for covering by fire known targets or targets of opportunity and by observation. Also called **AOR**.

Army corps. A tactical unit larger than a division and smaller than a field army. A corps usually consists of two or more divisions together with auxiliary arms and services.

assign. To place units or personnel in an organization where such placement is relatively permanent and/or where such organization controls and administers the units or personnel for the primary function, or greater portion of the functions, of the unit or personnel.

attach. (1) The placement of units or personnel in an organization where such placement is relatively temporary. (2) The detailing of individuals to specific functions where such functions are secondary or relatively temporary, e.g., attached for quarters and rations; attached for flying duty.

change of operational control. The date and time (coordinated universal time) at which a force or unit is reassigned or attached from one commander to another where the gaining commander will exercise OPCON over that force or unit. Also called **CHOP**. *See also* **operational control**.

combatant command. A unified or specified command with a broad continuing mission under a single commander established and so designated by the President, through the Secretary of Defense and with the advice and assistance of the Chairman of the Joint Chiefs of Staff. Combatant commands typically have geographic or functional responsibilities. Also called **COCOM**.

common servicing. That function performed by one military service in support of another military service for which reimbursement is not required from the service receiving support.

conventional mines. Land mines, other than nuclear or chemical, which are not designed to self-destruct. They are designed to be emplaced by hand or mechanical means. Conventional mines can be buried or surface laid and are normally emplaced in a pattern to aid in recording.

direct liaison authorized. The authority granted by a commander (any level) to a subordinate to directly consult or coordinate an action with a command or agency within or outside of the granting command. Direct liaison authorized is more applicable to planning than operations and always carries with it the requirement of keeping the commander granting direct liaison authorized informed. Direct liaison authorized is a coordination relationship, not an authority through which command may be exercised. Also called **DIRLAUTH**.

direct support. A mission requiring a force to support another specific force and authorizing it to answer directly to the supported force's request for assistance. Also called **DS**.

disposition. The operation by suitably qualified personnel designed to render safe, neutralize, recover, remove, or destroy mines.

explosive ordnance. All munitions containing explosives, nuclear fission or fusion materials, and biological and chemical agents. This includes bombs and warheads; guided and ballistic missiles; artillery, mortar, rocket, and small arms ammunition; all mines, torpedoes, and depth charges; demolition charges; pyrotechnics; clusters and dispensers; cartridge and propellant actuated devices; electro-explosive devices; clandestine and improvised explosive devices; and all similar or related items or components explosive in nature.

explosive ordnance disposal. The detection, identification, on-site evaluation, rendering safe, recovery, and final disposal of unexploded explosive ordnance. It may also include explosive ordnance that has become hazardous by damage or deterioration. Also called **EOD**.

Explosive Ordnance Reconnaissance Program. Reconnaissance involving the investigation, detection, location, marking, initial identification, and reporting of suspected UXO, by explosive ordnance reconnaissance agents, in order to determine further action.

forward arming and refueling point. A temporary facility organized, equipped, and deployed by an aviation commander. It is normally located in the main battle area closer to the AO than the aviation unit's combat service area, to provide fuel and ammunition necessary for the employment of aviation maneuver units in combat. The forward arming and refueling point permits combat aircraft to rapidly refuel and rearm simultaneously. Also called **FARP**.

functional component command. A command normally, but not necessarily, composed of forces of two or more military departments which may be established across the range of military operations to perform particular operational missions that may be of short duration or may extend over a period of time.

general support. That support which is given to the supported force as a whole and not to any particular subdivision thereof. Also called **GS.**

Global Command and Control System. Highly mobile, deployable C^2 system supporting forces for joint and multinational operations across the range of military operations, any time and anywhere in the world with compatible, interoperable, and integrated C^4 systems.

improvised explosive device. A device placed or fabricated in an improvised manner incorporating destructive, lethal, noxious, pyrotechnic, or incendiary chemicals and designed to destroy, incapacitate, harass, or distract. It may incorporate military stores, but is normally devised from nonmilitary components. Also called **IED.**

interoperability. (1) The ability of systems, units, or forces to provide services to and accept services from other systems, units, or forces and to use the services so exchanged to enable them to operate effectively together. (DOD). (2) The condition achieved among C-E systems when information or services can be exchanged directly and satisfactorily between them and/or their users. The degree of interoperability should be defined when referring to specific cases.

joint force commander. A general term applied to a combatant commander, subunified commander, or joint task force commander authorized to exercise COCOM (command authority) or OPCON over a joint force. Also called **JFC.**

joint operations. A general term to describe military actions conducted by joint forces (two or more services), or by service forces in relationships (for instance support or coordinating authority), which, of themselves, do not create joint forces.

joint operations area. An area of land, sea, and airspace, defined by joint forces, or by service forces in relationships (e.g., support, coordinating authority), which, of themselves, do not create joint forces. Also called **JOA.**

Joint Operation Planning and Execution System. A continuously evolving system that is being developed through the integration and enhancement of earlier planning and execution systems: Joint Operation Planning System and Joint Deployment System. It provides the foundation for conventional C^2 by national- and theater-level commanders and their staffs. It is designed to satisfy their information needs in the conduct of joint planning and operations. It includes joint operation planning policies, procedures, and reporting structures supported by communications and automated data processing systems. It is used to monitor, plan, and execute mobilization, deployment, employment, and sustainment activities associated with joint operations. Also called **JOPES.**

joint task force. A joint force that is constituted and so designated by the Secretary of Defense, a combatant commander, a subunified commander, or an existing joint task force commander. Also called **JTF.**

lead agent. Individual services, COCOMs, or joint staff directorates may be assigned as lead agents for developing and maintaining joint doctrine, joint TTP, publications, or joint administrative publications. The lead agent is responsible for developing, coordinating, reviewing, and maintaining an assigned doctrine, joint TTP, or joint administrative publication.

liaison. That contact or intercommunication maintained between elements of military forces or other agencies to ensure mutual understanding and unity of purpose and action.

line of communication. A route, either land, water, and/or air, which connects an operating military force with a base of operations and along which supplies and military forces move. Also called **LOC.**

logistic support. Logistic support encompasses the logistic services, materiel, and transportation required to support CONUS-based and worldwide deployed forces.

logistic support (medical). Medical care, treatment, hospitalization, evacuation, furnishing of medical services, supplies, materiel, and adjuncts thereto.

Marine air-ground task force. A task organization of Marine forces (division, aircraft wing, and service-support groups) under a single command and structured to accomplish a specific mission. The components normally include command, aviation combat, ground combat, and combat-service-support elements (including Navy support elements). Three types which can be task-organized are the Marine expeditionary unit, Marine expeditionary brigade, and Marine expeditionary force. Also called **MAGTF.**

Marine expeditionary unit. A task organization which is normally built around a battalion landing team, reinforced helicopter squadron, and logistic support unit. It fulfills routine forward-afloat deployment requirements, provides an immediate reaction capability for crisis situations, and is capable of relatively limited combat operations. Also called **MEU.**

Marine expeditionary unit (special operations capable).
A forward-deployed, embarked US Marine Corps unit with enhanced capability to conduct special operations. The unit is oriented toward amphibious raids, at night, under limited visibility, while employing emission control procedures. It is not a Secretary of Defense-designated special operations force but, when directed by the National Command Authorities and/or the geographical combatant commander, may conduct hostage recovery or other special operations under in extremis circumstances when designated special operations forces are not available. Also called **MEU(SOC).**

military operations other than war. Operations that encompass the use of military capabilities across the range of military operations short of war. These military actions can be applied to complement any combination of the other instruments of national power and occur before, during, and after war. Also called **MOOTW**.

military service. A branch of the armed forces of the United States, established by act of Congress, in which persons are appointed, enlisted, or inducted for military service, and which operates and is administered within a military or executive department. The military services are the United States Army, the United States Navy, the United States Air Force, the United States Marine Corps, and the United States Coast Guard.

mine. (1) In land-mine warfare, an explosive or other material, normally encased, designed to destroy or damage ground vehicles, boats, or aircraft, or designed to wound, kill, or otherwise incapacitate personnel. It may be detonated by the action of its victim, by the passage of time, or by controlled means. (2) In naval-mine warfare, an explosive device laid in the water with the intention of damaging or sinking ships or of deterring shipping from entering an area. The term does not include devices attached to the bottoms of ships or to harbor installations by personnel operating underwater, nor does it include devices which explode immediately on expiration of a predetermined time after laying.

munition. A complete device charged with explosives, propellants, pyrotechnics, initiating composition, or NBC material for use in military operations, including demolitions. Certain suitably modified munitions can be used for training, ceremonial, or nonoperational purposes. Also called ammunition. (Note: In common usage, munitions [plural] can be military weapons, ammunition, and equipment.)

noncombatant evacuation operations. Operations directed by the Department of State, the Department of Defense, or other appropriate authority whereby noncombatants are evacuated from foreign countries when their lives are endangered by war, civil unrest, or natural disaster to safe havens or to the United States. Also called **NEO**.

nuclear weapon. A complete assembly (i.e., implosion-type, gun-type, or thermonuclear-type), in its intended ultimate configuration which, upon completion of the prescribed arming, fusing, and firing sequence, is capable of producing the intended nuclear reaction and release of energy.

obstacle. Any obstruction designed or employed to disrupt, fix, turn, or block the movement of an opposing force and to impose additional losses in personnel, time, and equipment on the opposing force. Obstacles can exist naturally or can be manmade, or can be a combination of both.

operational control. Transferable command authority that may be exercised by commanders at any echelon at or below the level of COCOM. OPCON is inherent in COCOM (command authority). OPCON may be delegated and is the authority to perform those functions of command over subordinate forces involving organizing and employing commands and forces, assigning tasks, designating objectives, and giving authoritative direction necessary to accomplish the mission. OPCON includes authoritative direction over all aspects of military operations and joint training necessary to accomplish missions assigned to the command. OPCON should be exercised through the commanders of subordinate organizations. Normally this authority is exercised through subordinate JFCs and service and/or functional component commanders. OPCON normally provides full authority to organize commands and forces and to employ those forces as the commander in operational control considers necessary to accomplish assigned missions. OPCON does not, in and of itself, include authoritative direction for logistics or matters of administration, discipline, internal organization, or unit training. Also called **OPCON**.

operations center. The facility or location within a theater used by the commander to command, control, and coordinate all EOD activities. Also called **EOD**.

ordnance. Explosives, chemicals, pyrotechnics, and similar stores, to include bombs, guns and ammunition, flares, smoke, and napalm.

recovery. In naval-mine warfare, salvage of a mine as nearly intact as possible to permit further investigation for intelligence and/or evaluation purposes.

render safe. As applied to weapons and ammunition, the changing from a state of readiness for initiation to a safe condition.

Service component command. A command consisting of the service component commander and all those service forces, such as individuals, units, detachments, organizations, and installations under the command, including the support forces assigned to a COCOM, or further assigned to a subordinate unified command or JTF.

submunition. Any munition that, to perform its task, separates from a parent munition.

tactical control. Command authority over assigned or attached forces or commands, or military capability or forces made available for tasking, that is limited to the detailed and, usually, local direction and control of movements or maneuvers necessary to accomplish missions or tasks assigned. TACON is inherent in OPCON. TACON may be delegated to and exercised at any level at or below the level of combatant command. Also called **TACON**.

unexploded explosive ordnance. Explosive ordnance which has been primed, fused, armed or otherwise prepared for action. It has been fired, dropped, launched, projected, or placed in such a manner as to constitute a hazard to operations, installations, personnel, or material and remains unexploded either by malfunction or design or for any other cause. Also called **UXO**.

unit type code. A five-character, alphanumeric code that uniquely identifies each type unit, and, in the case of this manual, specific EOD organizations or structures of the armed forces. Also called **UTC**.

weapons of mass destruction. In arms control usage, weapons that are capable of a high order of destruction and/or of being used in such a manner as to destroy large numbers of people. Can be NBC and radiological weapons, but excludes the means of transporting or propelling the weapon where such means is a separable and divisible part of the weapon. Also called **WMD**.

REFERENCES

Joint

JP 0-2, *Unified Action Armed Forces*, 24 February 1995

JP 1-02, *Department of Defense Dictionary of Military and Associated Terms*, 24 January 2000

JP 3-0, *Doctrine for Joint Operations*, 1 February 1995

JP 3-07, *Joint Doctrine for Military Operations Other than War*, 16 June 1995

JP 3-07.2, *Joint Tactics Techniques and Procedures for Anti-Terrorism*, 17 March 1998

JP 3-07.5, *Joint Tactics, Techniques, and Procedures for Non-Combatant Evacuation Operations,* 30 September 1997

JP 3-15, *Joint Doctrine for Barriers, Obstacles, and Mine Warfare,* 24 February 1999

JP 5-0, *Doctrine for Planning Joint Operations*, 13 April 1995

JP 5-00.2, *Joint Task Force Planning Guidance and Procedures,* 13 January 1999

DOD Instruction 5030.34, *Agreement Between the United States Secret Service and the Department of Defense Concerning Protection of the President and other Officials*, 17 September 1986

Technical Manual (TM) (Army), Technical Order (TO) (Air Force), EOD Bulletin (Navy), 60A-1-1-7, *Explosive Ordnance Disposal Procedures; Field Evaluation and Intelligence*, 23 March 1999

Multiservice

AR 75-14/MCO 8027.1D/OPNAVINST 8027.1G/AFJI 32-3002, *Interservice Responsibilities and Procedures for Explosive Ordnance Disposal*, 14 February 1992

FM 3-100.38 (FM 100-38)/MCRP 4-5.1/NWP TP 3-02.4.1/AFTTP(I) 3-2.12, *Multiservice Procedures for Unexploded Ordnance*, July 1996 (Revision in progress)

FM 3-99.4 (FM 101-4)/MCRP 6-23A/NWP 3-13.1.16/AFTTP(I) 3-2.12, *Multiservice Procedures for Joint Task Force–Information Management*, April 1999

Army

NOTE: The new Army numbering system for field manuals reflects the new number, followed by the old number in parenthesis.

AR 75-15, *Responsibilities and Procedures for Explosive Ordnance Disposal,* 1 November 1978

FM 4-30.12 (FM 9-15), *Explosive Ordnance Disposal Service and Unit Operations,* 8 May 1996

FM 3-24.32 (FM 20-32), *Mine/Countermine Operations,* 30 September 1992

FM 4-30.11 (FM 21-16), *Unexploded Ordnance Procedures,* 30 August 1994

FM 3-34.2 (FM 90-13-1), *Combined Arms Breaching Operations,* 28 February 1991

Marine Corps

MCWP 3-2, *Aviation Operations,* April 1999

MCWP 3-16, *Techniques and Procedures for Fire Support Planning/Coordination,* March 1992

MCWP 3-17.2, *Explosive Ordnance Disposal,* December 1993

MCRP 3-17.2A, *UXO Procedures,* August 1994

MCWP 3-33.6, *Humanitarian Operations,* October 1994

MCWP 3-35.3, *Military Operations on Urbanized Terrain,* April 1998

MCO 3571.2, *Explosive Ordnance Disposal Program,* August 1990

Navy

Department of the Navy, *US Navy Explosive Ordnance Disposal Plan,* 28 March 1997

OPNAVINST 3501.97, *Projected Operational Environment and Required Operational Capabilities for Explosive Ordnance Disposal Ground Forces,* 26 January 1996

NWP 3-02.4, *Explosive Ordnance Disposal,* July 1997

Air Force

AFPD 32-30, *Explosive Ordnance Disposal,* 20 July 1994

AFMAN 32-3001, *EOD Program,* 1 June 1998

AFEOD Equipment and Supplies Listing, November 1998

Index

A

accident cleanup, A-1

administrative control, III-2, V-8 - V-9

administrative/logistics section, II-7

aerial port operations, VI-5

airborne mine countermeasures, V-6

Air Force, III-1, VI-3 - VI-4, A-1, D-3

Air Force Doctrine Center, ii

Air Land Sea Application Center, ii, ix

all-purpose remote transport system, VI-2, VI-6

amnesty program, III-6, E-3

amphibious ready group, V-1, V-3 - V-4

area search detachment, V-7, V-9

Army service component commander, III-3

B

base civil engineer, VI-1

base engineer emergency force, VI-2 - VI-3

base recovery after attack, IV-4

Bosnia, II-1, II-4

C

C^2, vi - vii, II-7, III-2, III-6, IV-1, V-2, V-4, VI-1, VI-3, C-1 - C-2, C-4

C^4I, V-8, C-4

chaplain, C-4

Chief of Naval Operations Instruction, see OPNAVINST

civil engineer, ii, ix - x, VI-2 - V-3, VI-5 squadron, VI-2 - V-3

combat rubber raiding craft, V-4, V-10, A-4

combat search and rescue, A-4

combat training centers, III-7

combatant command, i, C-4

command and control, see C^2

command, control, communications, computers, and intelligence, see C^4I

commander, amphibious task force, V-8

Commander in Chief, Pacific, E-2

communications-electronics, II-8

contingency plan, V-8, B-1, C-4

D

Department of State, III-6, VI-1, E-1

Desert Storm, II-1, V-8

detection, V-1, V-6 - V-7

direct liaison authorized, vii, II-2 - II-3, B-2, D-7

direct support, VI-5, E-2

dynamic entry, IV-5 - IV-6

E

engineer, III-1, III-7, VI-5, D-1 - D-2

engineer support battalion, IV-1 - IV-2, A-1 - A-4

exercise plan, B-1, C-4

expeditionary airfield, IV-3

F

Federal Bureau of Investigation, III-7, V-5

fleet antiterrorist security team, V-5

fly-away recompression chamber, V-7

force protection, I-1, III-3, III-6, IV-1, IV-4 - IV-5, VI-2, VI-5 - VI-6, C-2, E-2 - E-3

G

gas and oil platform, IV-5 - IV-6

general support, III-2, III-5

Made in the USA
Middletown, DE
30 January 2024

48789548R00126